THE STUFF OF LIFE
FACING CHALLENGES, LIVING LIFE WELL

Cover and Layout Design by James Norton
www.greenflashmedia.co.uk

First Published 2010 by:

Fusion UK, Revelation Centre, P.O. Box 58, Chichester, PO19 8UD

Company Registration No 3679369 Registered Charity No 1073572

ISBN 978-0-9539578-2-8

Foreword

Welcome to The Stuff of Life, it is the sort of stuff that affects all of us to a greater or lesser extent. It's stuff that already impacts our relationships and outlook on life, stuff that, if not faced, can diminish a lot of our freedom and enjoyment of day to day living. It's the stuff we often have a sense of shame about and struggle to talk about. It's the stuff that we often need a bit of help in working through. And it's the stuff that, once we have helped ourselves, makes us better equipped to help others.

My hope is that this handbook will bring fresh courage and hope to a generation of students and twenty-somethings; that the insights and understanding provided will give a framework for living life well; that areas of pain, weakness and addiction can be overcome and that the grace of God will be encountered in a new way. My hope also is that every young adult can read this handbook, first to better understand themselves, and second to better understand and appreciate others. It is this self awareness and awareness of others that is so important in twenty-first century mission. It allows us to meet people where they are and journey with them.

This is not self-help; it is about re-framing the challenges that life throws up, cultivating relational and emotional intelligence, and not letting our current emotional or mental pain be a barrier to our future fulfilment. I fully endorse the work of Mind and Soul [see page 92], not as something separate, but as a vital and integrated contribution for our health, spiritual formation and mission to this world. I am grateful Mind and Soul care enough to partner with Fusion in writing this handbook to encourage a generation of students and young adults sort out their 'stuff' and learn to live life well.

May it serve you well and also your friends who have yet to discover how very much God loves them.

Rich Wilson

NATIONAL TEAM LEADER, FUSION

Index

Opinions

Emotions are things people are passionate about. Some love to talk about them, some people have large chips on their shoulders, others are emotional deserts. Here are some opinions often offered by people:

Which of these quotes can you identify with?

Which ones do you think are helpful?

What would you say in reply to the ones you disagree with?

[By the way – we don't agree with all of them..! Ed]

"Am I the only person who feels like this? Everyone else seems fine..."

"Much of my DOING is motivated by the fact that I am less than at ease with my BEING"

"Jesus is the answer to all of life's problems – it's just a matter of perspective."

"I am fed up with easy answers to complex problems. It's just not that simple."

"I don't like large groups. I wonder if anyone will talk to me today?"

"Fear is just excitement on a bad day"

"Let me introduce you to me: content, confused, angry, sad, joyful, heartbroken, anxious me."

"Emotions are bad – my family always told me to control them"

About the Authors

Rob Waller

Dr Rob Waller is a Consultant Psychiatrist working for the NHS in Scotland. He is a Director of Mind and Soul and is passionate about getting Mental Health Services and Churches talking to each other.

He has spoken and written widely about the mental health of university students. He lives in Edinburgh with his wife Susanna and son James.

Will Van Der Hart

Revd Will Van Der Hart is the Vicar of St Peter's Church in West Harrow, London. St Peter's incorporates an NHS Christian Medical Practice and a healing prayer clinic. Will is a passionate Christian speaker and evangelist who also longs to see people set free from emotional health problems. He is a Director of Mind and Soul

Kate Middleton

Dr Kate Middleton is a Psychologist working in a church in Hertfordshire. Kate is a previous Director of Anorexia & Bulimia care and has written several books and articles on mental health issues. Her main interest is the way emotions can affect us, and the various unhelpful coping strategies we develop as a result. She has also been a student for 8 years so knows something about this topic!

Roger Bretherton

Dr Roger Bretherton is a Clinical Psychologist, and Senior Lecturer in Psychology at the University of Lincoln. He is an associate of Cantle Leadership Development, and on the wider leadership team of New Life, Lincoln. He is married to Marie-Claire and has two sons, Leo and Tomas.

Jonathan Clark

Jonathan Clark leads Premier Life, the community unit at Premier Christian Media containing the confidential helpline Premier Lifeline in addition to Premier Response and Premier Prayer Partners. He is a qualified Mental Health Social Worker and is one of the Directors of Mind and Soul.

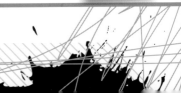

Staying Healthy
OF FIRST IMPORTANCE

Base Camp

Emotions are funny things. It's easy to think that in a perfect world we'd all be able to act independently of our emotions – that we'd be able to stop them from affecting us at all. You may have seen films about people, robots, aliens who do not experience emotions – and are portrayed as having a superior intelligence or ability to think clearly as a result. But, think of the emotional desert that is Daniel Craig as James Bond. In truth, this leaves us mere humans at war with our own true emotions. We try not to have them – not to react, not to feel the way we do, stop ourselves from ever showing them – but try as we might we cannot get rid of them.

The truth is that emotions are actually an essential part of the way our brains were designed. We cannot escape them, or avoid having them – because in fact they are really important, and without them our brains just don't work properly.

So what actually is an emotion? Can you remember the last time you felt a certain emotion – let's start with anxiety. What was it about how you were feeling then that makes you label it now and say it was 'anxiety'?

The anatomy of an emotion

Most people mention 4 key things that seem to be part of experiencing an emotion:

1. The first is some kind of **physical feeling**, like feeling butterflies in your stomach, or feeling your heart start to beat faster.

2. Then there's a sensation of wanting to **do something**. That might be something like run away, or stand up to someone. It might make you more likely to do something – like making you feel very fidgety.

3. Emotions also affect the way we think – triggering certain **thoughts** and drawing our attention to what is going on.

4. Then there is something else which is really hard to describe – **that elusive feeling** when you just know you are having an emotion.

These four elements that make up emotional experiences give us some great clues about what the point of them is.

Emotions are the brain's way of grabbing your attention

Emotions occur when certain combinations of things going on around you are identified as potentially significant – usually because they might affect your chances of achieving a goal stored within your brain. So that might be a basic goal like 'staying alive', or it might be something more complex like 'passing my exams' or grabbing lunch. If something happens which looks like it might have an impact on the chances of you achieving a goal – say you step out into the road and a bus is about to hit you – then your brain basically triggers an emotion to alert you.

Emotions try to get you to DO something!

An emotional response sets your body up in case you might need to react. So, having inadvertently stepped in front of that bus, you find yourself suddenly poised to jump out of the way, heart racing in case you need to run. Emotions don't make us act, but they do make us more likely to make a certain response. This is good if a bus is driving at you. But also, if something has made you angry, you are much more likely to shout at someone – even if it doesn't happen to be the person who made you angry in the first place.

Emotions influence our decision making

Because of the way we feel when we're experiencing an emotion, it influences how likely we are to consider certain options. Think about it - if you're faced with a decision that has a few options, and just thinking about one of them makes you feel incredibly nervous – you are much less likely to take that option. In this way emotions influence our decisions and help to simplify the bewildering array of choices we have to make every day.

Emotions are triggered when something significant is going on

Emotions can be unpredictable. In fact a bunch of people experiencing the same event can all react totally differently to it. You may have experienced that yourself – when something happens and you find it incredibly emotional, but someone else who is with you doesn't bat an eyelid. Emotions are triggered when your brain identifies something going on around you which might be significant – to you!

So your emotional reactions depend on things you've learned from past experiences as well as stuff going on for you now, and the hopes and dreams you have for the future. They also depend on the kind person you are. Some personality types leave us more prone to certain emotions or just more emotional in general. Some people's emotions are very visible, whilst others keep theirs more hidden. Emotions can be inconvenient, undesirable, leading you to feel things you'd rather not feel and do things you'd rather not do. But whoever you are, assuming you are human (and not Daniel Craig, as James Bond) you will experience emotion, whether you like it or not.

Looking to the Master...

We've all messed up at some time with our emotions – all had emotions we'd rather not have, or done things we wish we hadn't done. Knowing how to react and how to get the best out of our emotions isn't easy. But if you want to find an example of how to get it right there's an obvious place to look. Jesus is a great example of what it is to be human, and how to handle our emotions. Jesus was God made man – God in a human body – the body He designed! He was without sin – but still had emotions; so we know that the things he experienced are part of being a normal healthy human. We can also look at how he responded to his emotions and treat it as a kind of master-class.

Jesus experienced a whole range of emotions including love (Mark 10v21), grief (John 11v33-35), joy (Luke 10v21), anger (Mark 11v12-17), frustration (Mark 8v12) and sorrow (Matthew 26v37-38). Emotions like these are not sinful – but we do need to be careful about how we react to them. In some ways the biggest risk of emotions is that we will try to fight them – instead of just accepting them and trying to work out what is triggering them. Jesus always seemed to give himself the time and space to let his emotions out. Having said that, you wouldn't ever describe Jesus as being controlled by His emotions – they never overtook Him, or made him do anything wrong. Jesus calmly accepted his emotions and let them influence the way he responded to those around him. We can learn a lot from Him.

Freshers' Week

So – you've made it, finished school, passed your exams, and enjoyed some study-free time to chill out. But next comes one of the biggest challenges of your time at university – Freshers' Week! No matter who you are, starting Uni is a stressful experience – but it doesn't have to be a nightmare!

The Freshers' Week experience

If you are wondering what to expect, you'll find Freshers' week is an amazing and heady mix of parties, fantastic fun, staying up all night ... and standing in endless queues as you try to get everything sorted out for your course and accommodation! It's a unique opportunity to meet new people, as well as a chance to join new clubs and societies, make new friends and think about what is really important to you for your time at university.

Freshers' week is a very social time, and there will be lots of chances to go to parties, clubs, gigs etc. You may feel under pressure to be out every night, or find that you struggle to get any sleep at all. It can be rather intense, and sometimes it can feel like Fresher's Week is the be all and end all of university life. In fact it really is just the beginning. You will probably find you experience some mixed emotions about the whole thing. You may have spent months looking forward to leaving home, but find yourself feeling anxious about what living on your own or in student halls will really be like. Or you might be really looking forward to meeting new people and stuff, but be worried about missing your friends and family from home. It is totally normal to feel like this – really excited one minute, then dreading it the next!

Surviving Freshers' Week

First, remember that **it is totally normal to be daunted** by that first week at Uni. Very few people sail through Fresher's Week without a single misgiving, or negative feeling. With your normal support team miles away, you might find yourself feeling the odd pang of homesickness. If this happens then don't worry – it's totally normal! Right at the beginning of the Bible, God looks at the man He had created, and says 'it is not good for the man to be alone.' (Genesis 2v8). If you look at the Greek word that is translated as 'alone', it actually means to be 'cut off' or 'disconnected'. Humans are designed with a basic need deep within them to be connected with other people. That's why starting out and knowing no one can leave you feeling so lost. Those feelings will start to settle down once you get to know more people and put down some roots.

Second, **most people are not really quite as extreme as they appear to be** in Fresher's Week! All that nervous energy leaves lots of people acting in some slightly odd and over the top ways.

12

Try not to be alarmed! A quick survey amongst people I went to university with revealed some interesting week one reminiscences including:

- one person who accidentally introduced herself with the wrong name (and had to keep using it for quite a long time as a result)

- one who went to the wrong lecture hall for his first lecture and was too scared to admit it so sat through an hour of the wrong subject

- one who went to a party with some people from his hall, popped to the loo at one point, then couldn't recognise the group he'd come with when he got back, and

- another who drank too much the first night and was so scared of throwing up everywhere that he spend the entire night sleeping in the bath.

All of these people are actually very normal and nice and (I can vouch for them) not actually loopy at all. They all survived Fresher's Week and all made friends.

Third, remember that **you are not alone in finding this tough**. No matter how much people try to hide it, most of them are feeling as daunted as you. You probably feel convinced that no one would ever want to talk to you, but the truth is that most people will just be utterly relieved that someone is talking to them! Don't be afraid to make the first move. Remember the key questions that everyone will be asking – what's your name, where are you from, what subject are you studying, what A levels did you get - and try to think of some more interesting ones too. You could go with 'what animal would you like to be if you could choose anything' or maybe you can think of something better! It's well worth having a tactic for that initial first contact too. Try something as simple as offering someone a polo mint – it often works! Remember just because you talk to someone in Fresher's Week doesn't mean that you have to be best friends for the rest of your life. Don't put too much pressure on those early conversations and try to relax.

Fourth, **don't panic!** Remember Fresher's Week is actually just one week. In fact it's a pretty odd week and by no means is it a good measure of what the rest of university life will be like. If you get to the end of that week and feel like you know no one and want to go home, don't despair. Give yourself time, and give things a chance to settle down and form their own version of 'normal'. Then you will find people become much more chilled out and easier to get to know. Plus, as you feel more settled and start to know vaguely where you are and where you are supposed to be when, your own anxiety levels will drop, making it much easier to start to get to know people. Give yourself a break and try not to worry too much.

Do you recognise any of these people?

People try to handle the stresses of Fresher's Week in different ways. Have you met any of these yet?

THE PERPETUAL PARTIER. Possibly the most visible character in Fresher's Week, this person has listened to the message about wild and continuous partying, and taken it at its word. They are always to be seen at the biggest social gigs, and seem to have endless energy. Rarely spotted within daylight hours, they emerge with new confidence at around the same time as the bar opens.

THE COOL DUDE. Talk about dress to impress, this person has read all the [hidden] rules and got them in their blood. Never to be seen looking rough and ready, this person treats every new day on campus as a catwalk experience. They wear the right clothes, listen to the right music, eat or drink the right things. In fact, they look and act exactly the way you wish you could look and act. Trouble is, no one knows who they actually are, what they are really like, or even if they are real...

THE SPORTS FANATIC. A daunting sight, this person has found their confidence in sport, and can be easily recognised by their sports bag/equipment/university sports team sweatshirt. They have often played at county level in more than one sport, and probably go jogging several times a week. Conversations and social life alike revolve around sport and may be rather daunting when compared to your vague awareness of some of the rules of squash.

THE CLOWN. If you need to find the clown just follow the sounds of raucous laughter, because funny is what this person does. They have perfected over many years the skill of directing attention away from them, whilst still somehow remaining the centre of attention. They are a big fan of practical jokes and anything that makes other people look silly. The clown appears confident and may show no cracks in this flawless confident exterior. Underneath of course they are as scared as everyone else. Remember Coco and Krusty...

THE INVISIBLE (WO)MAN. This person is seized by a terror that people might notice them, only outweighed by the terror of what will happen if no one notices them. They aim to remain hidden and only go out when they absolutely have to. Social occasions are very hard, but they find solace in quiet places. Invisible (wo)men often claim to dislike loud places or social gatherings but often inside there is a much more confident person trying to get out.

THE SPACEMAN. Faced with the pressures of Fresher's Week this person has simply decided to try to pretend they are not there. Spaced out on some substance you may not be able to identify, they are difficult to engage in meaningful conversation, though strangely relaxing to be with. Easy to identify by their vacant expression, or by strange smells, empty beer cans or mysterious smoke coming from under their door.

THE ENTREPRENEUR. Often a variant of the serious student, entrepreneurs have been watching Dragon's Den and they are keen to make something of their university experience. Diligent attendance of all lectures, especially those following on from major parties or events presents a money making opportunity as entrepreneurs offer printed copies of their lecture notes for a small fee. This aids their popularity as they are often the only people with enough money to buy luxury items like food and decent wine.

Healthy Emotions

Emotions are all around us! Can you find 25 normal healthy emotions in this grid? When was the last time you experienced all of them?

T	N	F	E	A	A	A	Y	S	F	E	L	O	U	E
N	O	R	N	F	M	I	I	E	L	O	P	I	Y	D
E	I	U	T	O	U	U	A	R	V	T	H	I	I	Y
M	T	S	H	E	I	R	S	E	O	A	N	S	S	T
S	C	T	U	O	X	T	Y	E	P	H	G	T	A	E
S	A	R	S	L	E	C	A	P	M	U	P	E	D	I
A	F	A	I	I	O	Y	I	L	S	E	I	U	N	X
R	S	T	A	A	O	N	H	T	E	E	N	I	E	N
R	I	I	S	J	E	M	E	T	E	N	E	T	S	A
A	T	O	M	S	I	E	H	L	A	M	E	F	S	F
B	A	N	S	S	H	A	M	E	I	P	E	W	E	E
M	S	G	E	C	N	A	Y	O	N	N	A	N	R	I
E	R	R	E	G	N	A	Y	O	J	R	E	A	T	L
M	Y	F	E	I	R	G	L	T	I	O	U	S	S	E
A	A	N	O	U	F	M	M	N	D	E	E	A	S	R

amusement
anger
annoyance
anxiety
apathy
disgust
elation
embarrassment
enthusiasm
euphoria
excitement
fear
frustration
fury
grief
happiness
joy
loneliness
love
misery
relief
sadness
satisfaction
stress
shame

Emotions are one of the most powerful experiences about being human – and they are everywhere! There are thousands of words in every language which attempt to describe in some way what different emotions are. Normal, healthy emotions have vital roles in our everyday life. In fact people with injuries, illnesses or conditions that seem to affect their ability to feel emotion struggle terribly with normal everyday life. Emotions help us to relate to others, communicate how we are feeling, plan our time effectively, achieve our goals and make good decisions. Our emotions can also be a key part of our experience with God. The Holy Spirit can influence us through our emotions, moving us and triggering feelings of compassion (Eg Mark1v40-41), filling us with joy and praise (Luke 10v21) and sometimes just letting us know that something important is going on (Luke 24v32).

Having said that, it's only too clear that emotions can cause problems. We all know that sometimes our emotions lead us to do things that we think better of once we've calmed down. We must be careful about what our emotions lead us to do. Where emotions cause problems, it's the way we respond to them that is the trouble, not the emotion itself. So when exactly do emotions tend to cause problems?

Emotion sparks

Think of emotions like sparks that go off in your brain. If they work the way they are supposed to they are short-term bursts. They grab your attention – you analyse what is going on, decide if you need to take any action or not, and the emotion dies.

Emotions are designed to operate like this. But sometimes even sparks can cause problems. Imagine for example, that for some reason your brain is simply triggering too many sparks. Something about the way your brain is set up means that it is constantly having to warn you of potentially significant things going on. Maybe you are trying to live your life by goals that are just not possible – trying to be perfect all the time, or trying to get everyone to like you. Maybe life is throwing some crazy stuff at you and you are under a lot of pressure. During exam time for example, you are bound to be pretty stressed out and all those goals (all those subjects you need to pass!) might mean you get lots of sparks of emotion. Or, occasionally physical illnesses and problems can cause emotions to go haywire. This can result in too many sparks going off all at once and it can get to the stage where you simply can't deal with them all at once.

Emotional fires

Perhaps the most common way that emotions cause problems, however, has little to do with sparks. If you're struggling with your emotions right now it may be that what you're experiencing doesn't feel like sparks at all. You probably feel more like you are trying to fight fires – great big blazes of emotion. And that's pretty much what can happen. Remember the purpose of emotions is that they trigger us to think about what's going on and decide what we need to do. But sometimes they trigger thoughts that are nothing like that helpful. In fact sometimes the thoughts they trigger actually make things worse. These thoughts are like kindling – and if we're prone to thinking in certain ways, sparks of emotion can quickly build into something much bigger. It's like someone's struck a match in a dry forest – and those thoughts just act as kindling.

Suddenly you have an emotional blaze going which feels out of control and overwhelming. Emotional bonfires can rage on for a long time, meaning that emotions affect you for longer. Some people describe a kind of constant low level smouldering emotion that is always there and can blaze up without warning. These kinds of emotion are often linked with problems like depression and anxiety illnesses.

Emotional hijack

The final common problem with emotions comes when we have a very strong emotion reaction to something. Sometimes this is because something from our past has resulted in an emotion being triggered – linked as much to that memory as it is to what is going on now. Something happening now reminds you deep in your memories of something painful from the past and as a result your brain triggers a really strong emotion which might be out of proportion to what is going on now. Or you might have built up a strong emotional reaction to something over time – like what happens with fears and phobias.

When this happens, your brain actually has the option of bypassing the thinking region and just triggering the physical changes which lead to a reaction. So, often you only think after you have reacted, rather than before. This is appropriate if you had stepped in front of a bus (not much good standing there whilst you thought about what to do, much better to move first and think second), but perhaps not if you had run out of the room screaming something about a spider and it turned out that what you saw was really the green bit off the top of a tomato! This kind of 'hit first, ask questions later' reaction has been called emotional hijack and it can lead us to make some unfortunate decisions.

Suppressed emotions

Perhaps more than anything though, emotions start to become unhealthy when instead of dealing with them, we try to suppress them – push them down, pretend they don't exist and hope they go away. Answer this – if your job was to get someone's attention and they just ignored you would you go away? No – and neither do emotions.

Suppressing emotions doesn't work, and it can create a kind of bubbling pit of nasty emotions that you have never dealt with. Then, when you are alone, tired or vulnerable, and often when you least expect it, they emerge, and you suddenly feel terrible. These kinds of emotions can be powerful, overwhelming and scary, and have become separated from what actually triggered them in the first place, making them very hard to understand. Suppressing emotions means that you experience them behind closed doors – rather than connecting with other people and getting love and support. They are also the first stage in the development of many other problems as people desperately try to find some way of dealing with the intense feelings they are experiencing. Strategies that seem to help at first often end up causing more problems than they solve, leaving people with even more difficult emotions to deal with.

Suppressing emotions is like trying to put an angry cat in a box. It takes a lot of energy to keep it in, and there is always the fear it might get out at the worst time possible. And at some stage of course, you have to let it out – and then it's going to be pretty difficult to deal with.

Five top tips

Keep it simple! What are the five most important things I can do to stay emotionally healthy? This is our 'agony aunt' list. They may look simple, but cracking these is harder than it looks. PS – there are more than five, but five as many fingers as I have and this is a good list to start with.

Friends

Old-skool English poet John Donne (that'll be 1572-1631 to impress people) said, "No man is an island, entire of itself; every man is a piece of the continent, a part of the main." We all need people, even those of us who are introverts. Aim for a couple of close friends – and build these slowly over time, with love, sacrifice and laughter. Aim for a handful of 'mates' – who you see or talk to often. Allow as many others as you need to be at more of a distance – care for them, but don't expect too much and don't let them break your heart. And don't feel that you have to get on with EVERYONE all the time – the Bible never says this (see Romans 12v18 if you don't believe me!).

Fun

You'd be amazed at how seriously people can take the topic of emotional health. That's the main reason why this booklet is written in a relaxed style. We need to "get Jamaican on our emotions", and a large part of this is to stop trying so hard. If trying hard was going to work, it would have done so by now. So, take some time out from the planning, the prepping, the reviewing and the self-condemning – and have a bit of fun. It's time for a few belly laughs. You choose – as long as it is legal ;-)

Faith

Faith is the umbrella of life, the foundation of what we believe. Religion has been used over the ages to war, judge and condemn and the Latin word religio can mean 'bind' and 'restrain'. But it can also mean to 'bind up', to 'bind together' and to 'unite'. If we can leave behind the things of man and find the things of God, we will find faith, hope, love and most of all Jesus. Faith is good for our emotional health – it helps us keep perspective, it helps us find hope, it heals – it gives meaning to the suffering.

Food

It's hard to have good emotional health on a diet of chips and beer just as it's hard to have good skin. To be sure, there are some who never have a pimple or stress despite an awful diet – but for us mere mortals there is a clear correlation. You know the basics – a balanced diet and all that – but now it is time to actually put it into practice. Look at **www.5aday.nhs.uk** for the science and some healthy meal ideas? Why not cook for some of those friends you want to make?

Football – and other sports

Not everyone loves Beckham, so it's OK to replace football with ballet, swimming or good old walks in the countryside – they just don't begin with 'F'. Getting your pulse up makes you feel fitter, releases mood-enhancing endorphins and gives you something to talk about. Look at **www.nhs.uk/livewell/fitness** for some ideas, and **www.sustrans.org.uk** for the National Cycle Network.

Two vital tasks

Join a local church

No man is an island – see 'friends' on the previous page. An all are part of 'countries and continents'. For someone who wants to follow Jesus, this means being part of a local church.

- Unfortunately, there is no alternative to this. The local church is the pattern Jesus set up for Christian life and He does not intend us to follow him alone. Right at the beginning of the Bible, God said to Adam, "It is not good for man to be alone" and provided Eve. For the occasional lone missionary in the middle of some hypothetical jungle, it may be that there are no local believers. But for you and me in the UK this is not the case. We have a great blessing here with so many churches to chose from.

- Which type of church? Ideally one where other students go and with whom Fusion has a relationship – ask about this or visit **www.studentlinkup.org** for a list. However, one tip I would give is that the 'big bustle student church' many not be for everyone – especially if you are currently struggling with depression. I know many people in this situation who find a 'high church' that uses liturgy a good place to start as you can SEE and BE IN the truths more easily. Find a church where Jesus is the centre, the Bible is preached convincingly and people are valued as they are – those are the essentials.

- There are some who feel they have been hurt 'by church', but actually they haven't. They have been hurt by certain people at certain times. It is neither possible or helpful to be angry with a faceless institution like 'the church'. Instead, we need to identify the people, forgive them if we can, be reconciled with them if both parties can, and move on.

Register with a local GP

Many people go to University but never register with a local GP, instead preferring to keep on the books of the GP their family has always used – but this person is often miles away. But you can do both – students are allowed to have TWO GPs. This means that you can get prompt access to medical help if you need it.

If you have an existing medical condition (and this applies to mental health problems too), it is very important to let your new GP know so they can take this into account. You should also ideally have declared this on the 'confidential' section of your university application form so that Student Services are aware as they may be able to offer you extra support, 'academic dispensation' (extra time in some exams) and even a free lap-top. Students with more severe problems who need individual help may well be able to claim Disabled Students Allowance to cover the extra costs of getting this help – **www.direct.gov.uk** >> Disabled Students Allowance.

Spotting Problems
DO YOU RECOGNISE THESE PEOPLE?

Do you recognise these people?

They are all around us. We may even be one of them. In fact we probably are them some of the time; or several of them at once? None of us is perfect…

Stressed Steve

Steve is always anxious. After all, you never know what is going to happen in the future – so it's best to be super-prepared. Isn't it? Steve spends so much time living in the future that he is never really able to enjoy the present. This is a shame, because the present is just that – a gift for us to enjoy. Ok, awful pun but you get the idea. His anxieties sometimes come out as frank panic attacks or in avoiding social situations, but most of the time he muddles on through – never really participating.

Most likely to say: Better safe than sorry. It's always best to be prepared.

Get help: Page 33

Sad Sally

Sally is in some ways the opposite of Steve – she spends a lot of time thinking about the past and about some of the difficult things that have happened to her. They have shaped how she views the world and continue to shape the predictions she makes about the future – which are mostly negative. She says she lives day to day, but actually finds it hard to really enjoy the present.

Most likely to say: I can't see that ever happening. What's the point.

Get help: Page 45

Stoned Sam

Why work hard at university when you can party hard. Sam isn't quite as bad [in his eyes] as his mates who will inject anything they can lay their hands on, but he certainly never spends much time with a clear head. It all started off because he was seeking 'peace' and thought this would be found on a different level. But it wasn't there on a reliable basis and now he mainly takes the drugs to avoid the mess his life has become. Oh, and to avoid those awful feelings of coming down.

Most likely to say: This stuff isn't really that harmful. I can stop when I want to.

Get help: Page 54

Self-harm Sarah

Sarah started cutting because some of her friends were doing it. They told her that it would give her a buzz and take away some of 'the pain'. But Sarah has never told anyone about the pain she is trying to hide from – will she ever be able to share the secret? The problem with self-harm is that it works – for a while. But the other problems are the need to keep on doing it, the scars [which people are starting to notice] and the risk that she might do something more serious one day.

Most likely to say: It works. I deserve this.

Get help: Page 63

Psychotic Sid

Over the last two years, Sid has become increasingly withdrawn. He finds it hard to trust people and has even fallen out with his best mate. There is sometimes a voice in his head that tells him important things – but also some nasty things. There is nowhere to go for help as there isn't anyone to trust any more.

Most likely to say: This is real! How do I know I can trust you?

Get help: Page 71

Sexy Sue

Thank heavens for the 60s – people started dressing well. No more tweed, ties and tuxedos – it was OK to show a bit of skin. But people commented on the skin and said how nice it was (the first compliment she had ever received) so she showed some more and then some more. It all started with a bit of fun, but Sue is now preoccupied with how she looks and what others say – even to the point of being willing to give everything away to the man who asks for it. Sue doesn't feel very sexy anymore.

Most likely to say: Do you like this new dress? I hate the fact that people stare at my chest

Get help: Page 40

If you see yourself or others here, look for directions in the rest of this booklet. But remember this – we all have problems and we all need help. Please don't go 'problem spotting' in other people without first taking a good look at yourself – Jesus called this taking the plank out of your own eye… (Matthew 7v1-5).

And be careful how you talk to others about their problems – it can be very stigmatising and can label a relationship forever. It comes best from someone who has had the same problem themselves, and may even still be struggling. Also, not everyone wants to, is ready to or can listen to advice. The passage mentioned above from Matthew goes on to talk about 'not casting your pearls before swine' (verse 7) – so mention it once, maybe twice, then it's up to them.

Self Assessment

The first part of starting to change this is to know where you are starting from. This might sound obvious, but especially when you are feeling depressed it is like walking through treacle – everything is hard work and nothing is clear. It can seem oh-so-relative and there are no fixed things to push against. So here is something fixed – a snap-shot for today.

This test is called the PHQ-9 [Patient Health Questionnaire] and is used by doctors to rate how serious problems are - see more at **www.phqscreeners.com**. You should complete the questionnaire again [maybe online] in a few weeks to see if things have changed.

	Not at all	Several days	More than half the days	Nearly every day
	0	1	2	3
Little interest or pleasure in doing things				
Feeling down, depressed, or hopeless				
Trouble falling asleep, staying asleep, or sleeping too much				
Feeling tired or having little energy				
Poor appetite or overeating				
Feeling bad about yourself, feeling that you are a failure, or feeling that you have let yourself or your family down				
Trouble concentrating on things such as reading the newspaper or watching television				
Moving or speaking so slowly that other people could have noticed. Or being so fidgety or restless that you have been moving around a lot more than usual				
Thinking that you would be better off dead or that you want to hurt yourself in some way				
Totals				
Grand Total				

 If you have more than five ticks in the two right hand columns or you have ticked anything except 'Not At All' in answer to the last question, you should **get some professional help**. See page 75 for information on how to do this.

Students and Mental Health
BEAUTIFUL MINDS

Crisis Point

Imagine the situation – every year over a million people in the UK move away from friends and loved ones to live in close community with people they do not know, studying courses that will stretch them far more than ever before, and making decisions and life choices that will affect the rest of their lives. Many are carrying burdens already from broken homes, early experiences and family debt. Many also carry the expectations of their parents and teachers – not to mention the expectations they lay on themselves.

These people are students – these people are you! Is it any wonder that mental health problems are twice as common among students that they are among other of a similar age. Most students currently come from (fairly) privileged backgrounds, but with government targets of having 50% of 18-30 year olds in higher education, there will be increasing numbers of people from less fortunate backgrounds – with a consequentially higher rate of mental health problems.

Common problems

There is a myth that all students are smiling and happy – after all, they are often seen as having a cushy lifestyle with none of the stress that 'real people' with jobs have. There is the obvious reply that many students have both jobs and dependent children, but even for those living the supposed student dream, the rates [1] of emotional and mental health problems are high.No space to learn

Problem	Student Population	Similar General Population
General Emotional Ill-Health [2]	29%	16%
Anxiety	34%	13%
Depression	13%	11%
Eating Disorder	10%	4%
Drink over Government limits	Male: 61%, Female: 48%	Less than 40%
Substance Misuse	Greater than 50%	Less than 25%
Have considered suicide [3]	33%	

With these ongoing problems, it is perhaps no surprise that students are finding it hard to study. Having mental health problems affects our ability to complete university, the class of degree we may get and the chance we have of finding a job after university. University is a unique chance to get help for these problems through skilled and well-resourced Counselling Services and GP practices.

[1] Data from **www.osmhn.org.uk** >> Research Findings

[2] More than one standard deviation below the norm on the General Health Questionnaire

[3] More info from **http://cebmh.warne.ox.ac.uk/csr/**

Love Your Mind

Emotional and mental health issues affect everyone in some way. At least 25% of students will suffer personally from a mental health problem in their lifetime. There was once a time in church history when Christians were at the cutting edge of mental heath care, but sadly we have both become ignorant of the issues and marginalised by an increasingly 'professionalized' society.

Mental and emotional health issues are increasingly prevalent and the student population is often heavily affected. Many students find the stresses and pressures of new living situations, finances and work overwhelming. Stress, anxiety and depression are particular common problems.

Love Your Uni

'Love Your Uni' is an awesome initiative to show the students the love of Jesus and allow their actions and attitudes to say as much as our words. See more at **www.loveyouruni.org**. 'Love your mind' is a natural extension of this.

The majority of people who have suffered from an emotional or mental health issues have also felt a stigma or shame attached to having a disorder. This cultural problem greatly exacerbates both the suffering of the individual and length of time before they get treatment. Commonly sufferers are reluctant to seek medical help, or break the silence of isolation because of the fear of the reactions they may receive. Students who are suffering need really caring, well-informed and reliable support.

It would be wonderful if Christian students with an interest, took it upon themselves to become educated in the area of mental and emotional well being and could demonstrate the love to Jesus to this suffering in this way.

What could you or a group of students do this term at your University?

- put on a mental health awareness event in the bar

- ask the Counselling Service how you could help

- offer yourself as volunteer supporters to students with more severe mental health problems who need 1-2-1 support

loveyouruni.org

But before you do something like this...

UNDERSTAND YOURSELF: learning about your own mental and emotional identity is a really important way of offering help to others. Working in this area really requires that you hold a holistic view of personhood; body, mind and spirit. It is easy to marginalize people who are suffering with a mental health issue and lose sight of the whole person, if you understand yourself holistically you will be much better at supporting others.

BE BALANCED IN YOUR APPROACH: Sadly well meaning Christians can often inadvertently cause great pain and suffering or those who have a mental health problem by seeing the cause as being completely spiritual. In the same way as with physical problems, emotional and mental health problems have roots in chemistry and biology as well as the heart and spirit. Christian supporters must comprehend the medical and psychological roots of mental health issues as well as their spiritual interpretation.

BE A CONFIDENTIAL SIGN-POSTING SERVICE: Helping others who are struggling is not about becoming an expert yourself. It is about knowing how to support and encourage someone to the right sort of help. The best advice you can give is to encourage someone who is struggling to see their GP or student mental health services. If you know where to send someone and how to talk with them through their process of healing you will be being and amazing support.

BE PATIENT: In a world that demands instant results, 'Loving people's minds' requires a counter-cultural approach. Patience and consistency of support are by far the most loving way to help someone.

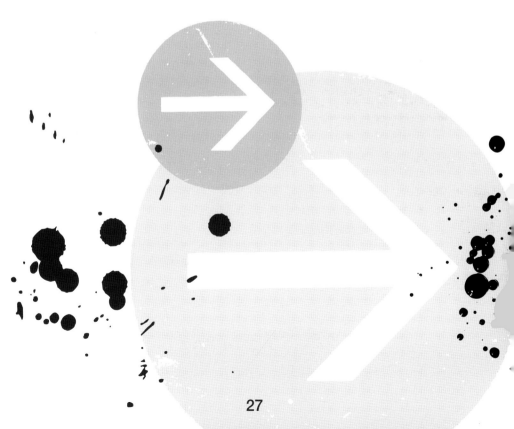

Things not to say and what to say/do instead

People say the stupidest things! Some people are downright rude and offensive, others say things with the best of motives but still manage to put their foot in it – because they have not thought through how the other person will receive what they are saying.

So, just what do you say to someone who is feeling down? The second list gives some ideas. Look at how they are different. Often they avoid talking about emotions directly (people can easily try to become amateur psychoanalysts), or they suggest something other than talking – which is often easier on a person who is struggling with their emotions.

What not to say (and what people think when you do)

Pull yourself together *(makes it seem like they are not trying already)*

Snap out if it *(if I could have I would have)*

We all feel like this sometimes *(no we don't, you have no idea)*

Have you tried praying about it? *(er, Yep. I've been a Christian for ten years…)*

You are a hypochondriac / needy person *(are you saying I am enjoying this?)*

Why can't the doctors help? *(I must be really broken – they have helped others)*

What to say/do instead (and why they are good things to say/do)

If you want to talk, I'm here to listen *(I care about what's happening to you and need to listen to you as a friend to show you that. Then I can understand and help you. I realise this may take some time – and I am going to stand with you.)*

I'm praying for you. Do you want me to pray for you now? *(I don't have any magic answers and I'm not trying to give you one but what I can do is pray for you. I know God hears prayers.)*

I have some practical wisdom I can share with you. *(Because I've spent time with you and listened to you, I can see you need rest, space, food, spiritual advice etc and may be able to help you.)*

I have no idea what it must feel like because I've never suffered from mental illness but I can understand it better now. Thank you! *(Trying to put yourself in someone else's shoes shows you appreciate them even if you don't fully get it.)*

Shall we go out together somewhere? Can I offer to pay if money is tight? *(Special times with friends help and if I can help take you out for a while it may help you escape from the same surroundings and focus on something else. I know that sometimes money can be tight when you are not working, so please let me know if this is the case and I can pay this time.)*

I can see you're not feeling great at the moment; do you want me to go away and come back tomorrow or another day? *(I can appreciate that if you're having a really bad day, I should come back another time and I'll be able to help better. You can decide. You don't have to explain – just say "Not now, thank you.")*

Talk to them about something positive in their life, or an improvement that you've noticed. *(Sometimes when you are so in the middle of something and experiencing it every day you can't see the small improvements that are happening or recognise an achievement or progress.)*

Find out any likes, hobbies, what makes them laugh and work towards helping them achieve one of these. *(Laughter is good medicine, we all need purpose in our lives and to feel we're achieving something. Would you like to help me with this jigsaw I am doing or go to the cinema?)*

Where Mind Meets Soul

We like to live our lives in boxes – what happens on the lecture theatre is not related to what happens with my boy/girlfriend and similarly is not related to what happens in my Fusion Cell Group... Obviously Fusion want to encourage you to think in a more balanced and [w]holistic way. What happens in your walk with God is meant to be the pulse of everything else in your life – your compass, your vision and your goal.

But when it comes to integrating ideas like Christianity and Mental Health problems, there is a pretty poor history of doing it well. The problems go something like this:

- Jesus has sorted out everything and you are meant to be happy

- Never talk about emotions. Never did at home, so why do so at church?

- If you had enough faith you could make this go away and be healed

- Mental Health Problems are not mentioned in the Bible so we won't talk about them

- Everything is about evangelism – what goes on in your head is irrelevant

I hope you haven't been on the receiving end of too many ideas like this, but here is an explanation of why these ideas came about, how to answer the more common errors and lastly a vision of how these two things can be beautifully and helpfully integrated. If you don't like history or theology, skip to the next page ;-)

The Great Divide

About 300 years ago, give or take a century, something called the Enlightenment happened. It was the age of men and science, of advancement and empire. Reason was king and, given enough time, humanity would sort out all the world's problems. From philosophy by Kant and Descartes came novels by Jules Verne, politics by Benjamin Franklin and the founding of the Royal Society of London.

In our universities, a division arose between those disciplines thought to reflect reason and experimentation (mainly the sciences – and the BSc was born) and those thought to relate to internal reflection (mainly the arts – and the BA was reborn). This division has existed to this day and you don't need to be a genius to work out that Medicine (and the study of heath) was a Science while Divinity (and the study of the soul) was an Art.

This, of course, is a simplification. Hippocrates said of medicine "The Art is Long" and there is certainty a lot of uncertainty in the complex world of the human body; and the soul is not a place where the laws of science suddenly break down – after all, did not God create these laws?

Psychiatry (and the study of mental health) sits right on the cusp. It spans all the way from neuroscience and brain scanning to psychoanalysis and ethics. I studied as a doctor, read Freud [who got a Nobel Prize for Literature by the way] and if I had my time again might read History at University.

The extreme statements above are made by people who don't know their history and haven't stood back to see the bigger picture. Churches were suspicious of science and have never really engaged – and so fuelled atheism. Some scientists think that if you can't put it in a test-tube then it isn't real – but what about true love? Some Christians turn to one God on Sunday and another god during the week.

I'm not supposed to feel like this

One of the first things that goes through the head of a Christian who gets depressed is that this is not meant to be happening. This is partly because they think that when Paul says in Philippians 4v1 "Rejoice in the Lord always" he means that we should wear a cheesy grin. But it is also because they are terrified of the reaction they may receive if they open their mouth. In many churches, sadly, success and achievement are rewarded as in many other areas in life and anything seen as weakness is avoided, ignored or worse still castigated.

What a contrast with our Saviour who made time for the poor and the needy, of whom it was said, "a bruised reed he will not break and a smouldering wick he will not snuff out" [Isaiah 42v3], and who knew despair and suffering, sadness and bereavement, tears and scars. When we cannot be open about our emotions then we are doing something wrong. Christianity does have relevance to our emotions, but we should never be in a position where we feel we should or should not behave a certain way just because others don't know how to respond and haven't followed the example Jesus set.

Wealth and Mental Health

Prosperity Theology has been part of the church for as long as anyone can remember. One of the main reasons the church grew so fast in the first centuries was that it offered a cheap and easily accessible form of healing through prayer – sacrificing a pair of oxen was expensive and messy! The church took over medicine for the next thousand years; as monasteries ran hospitals and shrines healed the sick. It's no wonder then that Christianity and Health became linked.

And linked they are – God longs to heal and has given us tools for healing in the church and prayer. But the relationship is not a law that is 1-2-1 or a 'transaction' – you cannot put faith into one end of the machine and get healing out of the other. Christianity is a relationship and 'God is no man's debtor', as CS Lewis said. Prosperity Theology is a great thing to believe when life is going well as it makes you feel good, as though life is going somewhere because of you and what you do for God. But when the wheels come off or life throws you a lemon you can't catch, then it comes round and bites you on the bum (if you will pardon my mixing of metaphors). You feel sad, useless and very, very alone. Not a good place to be. Especially if you are depressed. So beware prosperity theology.

The Functional Saviour

People have become Christians for all kinds of reasons. They thought the music was cool, their gran recovered from cancer or they got that great new job. God doesn't care how people come into the Kingdom, but He does care on what terms they stay. These reasons are all fragile and temporary and will leave you asking for more and more. And this asking will lead you to one day be disappointed.

When Jesus is no more than a Functional Saviour we turn to when we need X or Y but never really worship just for who He is, we will never truly get to know the real Jesus. Functional Jesus is always at the mercy of a better offer or a tough challenge and will never see you through when tough times come. Some Christians [not all] are unhappy because they are asking God for stuff he never promised to deliver and may not really want to – not on those terms, anyway.

The Gift of Grace

Christianity contains this amazing concept of Grace. Literally – God's Riches At Christ's Expense. But for all you can come up with neat mnemonics or accurate theology, Grace in my view is best understood as a dance; a relational flow between two people who think the world of each other – you and God. When grace is in charge, hurts are forgiven, folly is put into perspective and people build each other up. When grace is in charge, differences can be amazing, challenges can be overcome together and the present can be fully enjoyed.

Most importantly in the context of this booklet, when grace is in charge we can tackle tough topics like emotions and faith without people leaping to conclusions and adopting stigmatising and belittling attitudes. When grace is in charge the broken are bound up without an immediate and guilt-inducing expectation of snapping out of it. When grace is in charge the addict is just one kind of sinner – and we are all sinners.

When grace is in charge, Mind can talk to Soul in ways that are tolerant, creative and expectant...

Stress & Anxiety
WHATEVER YOU DO, DON'T PANIC

Exams

The University Year has certain key times of stress like Freshers' Week, but also Exam Time. Many courses have some continuous assessment, which can add to the pressure students feel they are under, but even so things tend to come to a head at the end of each semester – in the New Year and just after Easter. Not even the promise of long summer breaks can help, as this is also stressful for some people!

Planning for exams

'A stitch in time saves nine' – you may think I am sounding like your mother, but this is a true saying. A little bit of preparation can go a long way.

- Get some help from your Universities study skills centre – many people, especially mature students, feel very out of practice when it comes to exams and essays

- Make a revision diary – work out how many modules/lectures you have to cover and set a maximum time per module/lecture so you don't run out of time

- Leave some slack in case some things take longer than you expect or something unexpected comes up, like a family illness

- Arrange to meet with one or two course mates to compare ideas and 'hot topics' – share the work of planning for these by sharing essay outlines

Procrastination

I had the most wonderful revision diary when I was at University. The trouble was it took me three weeks to make and by then it was out of date! Putting off unpleasant tasks is common – they are unpleasant, other things are more attractive and it can give you an 'excuse' if you do badly as 'you didn't work much'. However, it will mean you get worse results. Try some of these tips: break down the work into manageable bits, give yourself treats as you go along, try different strategies – mind mapping, colours, sitting outside or in the library. But please make a start...

Concentration

Do you find your mind wandering? Hard work does not have to be continuous work, especially if you plan ahead, so: take regular breaks [this varies for each person so do what works for you], use a technique like saying STOP out loud if you find your mind wandering [but you may not want to do this in the library!], allow a little time for 'worrying' each day – this is OK, use active learning techniques [organise, mind-map, categorise, tabulate, summarise, discuss – don't just read].

Exam panic

It's the big day or maybe the night before and you are a bag of nerves – sweaty, nauseated, trembling... You find some good relaxation techniques on the next few pages so try these, but you may also want to:

- Arrange to walk to the exam with a friend, or plan a meal afterwards. Don't talk work!

- Avoid too much caffeine the night before – sleep will help more than that last cramming session. Cramming also fills your brain with the most recent detail, obscuring other things you know.

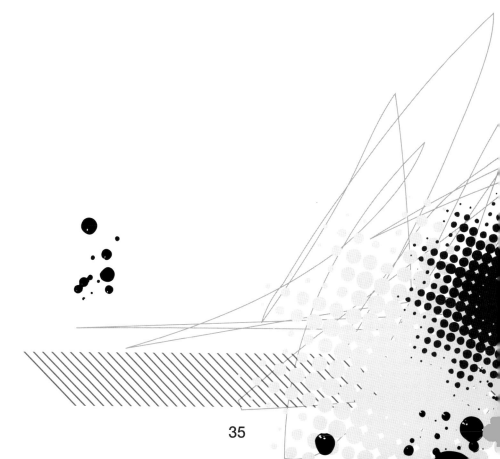

Panic Attacks

Did you know that 10% of the student population experience occasional panic attacks and an even larger number of adults in the UK will have experienced a panic attack at one time or another (NHS). It is also extremely common for the individual to head straight to the hospital during or following their first attack. They think they are going mad or are going to die!

The thing about panic attacks is that there are a cocktail of psychological (mind) and physiological (bodily) responses. The student environment can be very stressful and it is this stress that really precipitates the attacks. When you really understand them they loose some of their power, and you can learn to stop or minimise them.

The really frightening thing about having panic attacks is their unpredictability. Some people move from the experience of having one or two panic attacks in a few years to something called Panic Disorder, where sufferers might have several attacks per day or night.

Common symptoms experienced during a panic attack are: [4]

- dizziness or feeling faint

- palpitations or increased heart rate

- sweating, trembling or shaking

- difficulty breathing

- feeling of choking or nausea

- chest pain

- numbness or tingling sensations

- chills or hot flushes

- feelings of unreality and detachment

- fear of losing control

- fear of dying

- a sense of great danger and an urge to escape

This is not an exhaustive list, so if you are experiencing other sensations don't be concerned that they aren't mentioned here. Panic attacks are actually a result of what is known as 'the fight or flight' response. We really need this response in our lives; it is what makes us run from attackers or bears or other dangers. If we didn't have it we wouldn't last that long. But if you think about it, the response isn't conscious – it is instinctual. We don't stop to consider if a man's gun is loaded or just a toy – if it is pointed at us we are out of there. Panic attacks are just the 'fight or flight' response kicking in when there is an inappropriate stimulus. Most commonly panic attacks are actually a result of frightening thoughts that trigger a stressed nervous system into panic. This panic then causes another flow of frightening thoughts like, 'I am going mad', which in turn trigger more attacks.

[4] list from www.nhs.uk with permission

Afraid of fear

I don't know what is worse with panic attacks: the feeling of fearing they are about to happen or the actual attack. Whichever you find hardest to cope with, you can be sure they are both there. If we fear the fear, we get the symptoms and if we fear the symptoms we get the fear. The bottom line is that fear is the result and the initiator of the symptoms.

There are a few things you need to know. Firstly, you are not going mad, which is a relief. Secondly, whilst attacks are unpleasant, they are not actually detrimental to your health and are not causing any damage to your brain or heart. Thirdly, unwitting hyperventilation when you stressed or fearful is a major contributor to panic attacks. If you can stop hyperventilating then you can deactivate the attacks before they can happen (by stopping the over oxygenation of the brain which causes the symptoms). The best antidote to panic is to aggressively relax.

Overcomers

Overcoming panic attacks can take time and practice. Try to embrace every attack as an opportunity to experiment on what stops them. Try to laugh at your attacks while they are happening; make them smaller and less serious than they are now. I know this sounds hard, but it works! Life is a tough journey and for some people panic attacks can be an additional hazard. Remember that you are a child of God, you are not the sum of your attacks, they do not represent any terrible weakness, or any sinful lack of faith. They are just there right now. It has been ok, it is ok and it will be ok. God is with you, in every moment.

Practical tips:

1. Do go to see your GP to discuss your attacks. Try and go armed with a diary of how frequently they have occurred and note their intensity and length.

2. Avoid reading tons of internet sites - some are just plain wrong. The ones linked to from the Mind and Soul links page are the best place to start – **www.mindandsoul.info** >> search for 'panic attacks' or 'anxiety'.

3. Don't be ashamed of them. They are common and most people will know what you mean.

4. Pray about them, invite God to lead you away from them. (Be cautious if people claim to have 'broken' them or 'freed' you from them   they are not spiritual, they are behavioural.)

5. Aggressively relax when you feel the warning signs of an attack coming on. It feels like they come on just like that, but actually there is a build up so watch for the early signs of tension.

6. Create lots of relaxation space in your life and engage in meditating on the Lord and his peace.

7. Don't stop doing anything you would normally do because of your attacks or begin to live defensively, instead fly in the face of them. You also need your usual activities to keep your mood up.

8. Try not to see attacks as 'setbacks' or 'failures'.

9. Remember that their frequency will decline as your system begins to regard them as insignificant. This will take time, like any learning process.

10. Your stress system is working correctly – just not appropriately. It just needs re-training and re-calibrating.

Other Anxieties ↗ ↖

Post-traumatic Stress Disorder [PTSD]

According to a recent study 50% of us, if we haven't already, will have to live through trauma: a road traffic accident, a physical assault, a fire, a flood, a terrorist attack... the list goes on. The reason a statistic like that seems shocking or morbid is because generally speaking we don't like to think about trauma that way. We carry all kinds of assumptions about how, when and to whom disaster will happen. We may think that we're somehow immune to disaster; that it happens to other people, but not to us. We may think that the world is fair, and therefore bad things don't happen to people who don't deserve it. Or we may think that things always make sense and can be predicted. Most of the time we're not even aware we've made these assumptions about life, until they're shattered by a trauma.

Straight after a traumatic event, we are driven to make sense of what has happened. We think or dream about the event without wanting to, almost as if it's happening all over again. But thinking about it is painful, so we try our best not to. We avoid activities, stop going to places, or withdraw from people that remind us of what happened. We feel trapped between needing to make sense of it, and trying to avoid the pain caused by thinking about it. We feel as if the event is still stalking us, so we're nervous, jumpy, sleepless and constantly alert.

Believe it or not, all of these symptoms, while highly disturbing, are actually a normal response to a traumatic event and, for most people, they calm down after 4-6 weeks. However, for some people (usually about 25-30%) these symptoms don't go away of their own accord. This is what we call Post-traumatic Stress Disorder (PTSD), and it requires professional help.

Obsessive-Compulsive Disorder [OCD]

Obsessions are distressing thoughts, images or impulses that spring to mind uninvited. Compulsions are behaviours, like counting, checking or cleaning, that we feel driven to perform like a ritual or a regular routine. We all experience obsessions and compulsions, but when people find themselves caught in an unbreakable cycle of compulsive behaviour, like the student who compulsively cleans his room over and over again so the hall of residence doesn't get swine flu, we call it OCD. Psychological treatment for OCD tends to encourage people to endure the anxiety evoked by their obsessive thought, while reducing their compulsive behaviour and challenging the supposed harm that will result. It's a difficult disorder to overcome. There are some self-help materials available, but extreme cases will need professional support.

Social Phobia

Social phobia could be considered an extreme form of shyness. It becomes especially noticeable in student culture, where people are expected to share halls or flats, to meet in seminar groups and to socialise. If we suffer from social phobia, entering a room full of people triggers the kind of fear usually experienced in life-threatening situations. In extreme cases, socially phobic people will withdraw from everyone around them, sometimes never leaving their bedrooms. Good friends may be able to help them face their fear of other people, but if someone is extremely isolated, they may need to seek help from a professional.

Chronic Fatigue

Fatigue often occurs during long periods of stress, as a general deterioration in functioning. People feel tired all the time, struggle to concentrate or make decisions and, if accompanied by a severe lack of sleep, can even hallucinate or succumb to paranoia. It's not unusual to see students at exam time, suffering from some, or all, of these symptoms. They are, however, warning signs that the body's needs are not being met. Unless addressed immediately, with rest and a balanced diet and graded exercise, fatigue can get worse and even lead to hospitalisation.

How Do I Look?

If I could give one piece of advice for psychological wellbeing it would be: DO NOT compare yourself to anyone else. Catch yourself doing it? Stop it immediately. It only leads to trouble.

The Temptation to Compare

We often compare ourselves to other people as a way of judging how we're doing. Are we good-looking enough? Have we achieved enough? Are we popular enough? Are we influential enough? The list of possible comparisons is endless. If we feel we're doing slightly better than the people around us, we feel reassured that we're okay. This is the temptation – we hope to come off quite well in the comparison. Unfortunately any esteem we gain in comparing ourselves to other people is fundamentally insecure. There's always a bigger fish; always a better-looking group; always a more successful person. The high we get through favourable comparison is short-lived, and ties us to the low that arrives when someone beats us at our own game. Even when we come off well, rating ourselves against other people stores up trouble for the future.

Comparing Bodies

Nowhere is this more true than when we compare our bodies with those of other people. Traditionally this has been more of a problem for women, but increasingly it's becoming a problem for men too. At it's most basic level it's an attempt to keep up with the trends, to look as good as possible, and be admired or accepted by our peers. It's still not a great idea to hang our self-worth on mascara, running or hours spent in the gym, but for many people the distress caused by this kind of comparison is relatively minor. It is still avoidable, though – if we stop comparing.

But when body-comparison gets linked to self-hatred, the misery involved enters a different league. Most people who hate their bodies have been taught to do so by their personal history. Physical/sexual abuse and extreme bullying/victimisation are all possible candidates for teaching us that our bodies are bad. For some people, one part of their body gets the blame for all their problems. They start to think that if their nose weren't so big, their legs not so short, their ears not so protruding, or whatever, then everything would be okay.

For those with cash to spare, this can led to extensive cosmetic surgery, which almost never delivers the lasting self-acceptance or confidence they hoped for. Other people get stuck in a deadlock, attributing much of their distress to a part of their body they can't change. Very often this part of the body gains exaggerated proportions in their mind. They think of it as bigger (or smaller), fatter (or thinner), and generally more noticeable than it really is. We all do this to a certain extent, but in its extreme form, it's called Body Dysmorphic Disorder (BDD) and usually requires some appropriate professional help.

What Can We Do About It?

In less extreme cases of body comparison, some of the following may help:

1. Make a decision to stop comparing yourself with other people (positively or negatively)- it does you no good. If you have faith, you may like to remind yourself that God loves you just as you are – He didn't screw up when he made you.

2. Learn to love your body. Choose to do body-positive activities. Pamper yourself with a warm bath and scented candles, go swimming, fly a kite, have a duvet day – do whatever it takes to tell your body that you love it.

3. Act against your shame. Look in the mirror and decide to accept what you see. If you rely on clothes and/or make-up; go out with a little less make-up than usual, or wear slightly informal clothes to a formal event. Keep doing it until you no longer feel ashamed.

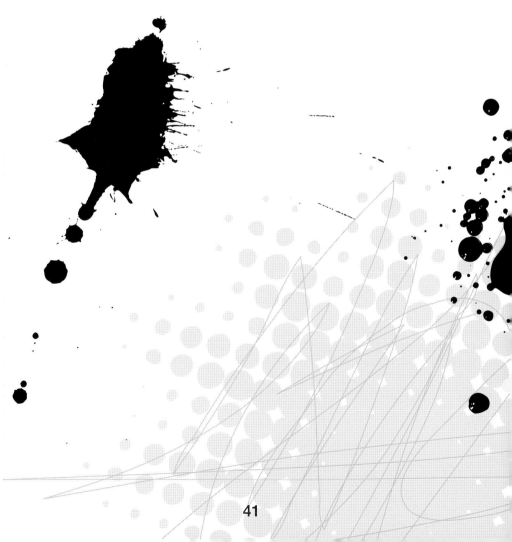

Eating Disorders

Whether it's through media articles, labels in the supermarket or just comments from friends, it's pretty difficult to get through a day without being questioned in some way about what you are eating or what you weigh. Issues around food are hugely common and it's hard to escape feeling slightly paranoid about what you look like with magazines full of airbrushed and idealised celebrity bodies. Studies suggest that less than a quarter of women are happy with their bodies; food and weight issues don't pass guys by either. In fact some research suggests that up to a quarter of eating disorders sufferers are men.

Lots of us have issues around food or what we look like – but when does this become a real problem? Eating disorders occur when the usual milder obsessions, dieting fads or paranoia becomes really serious – and there is evidence that university students may be particularly at risk.

Eating disorders can affect anyone! They begin when someone who is struggling with difficult feelings and emotions starts to become obsessed with their weight or eating. They may think about it all the time, and feel that other things in their life would be different if only they could lose weight and regain control of their eating. They set themselves strict diets and form rigid rules about which foods are not allowed in an attempt to lose weight. Succumbing to temptation and eating a 'forbidden' food leads to horrendous feelings of guilt and anxiety. Only succeeding, sticking to the very limited food planned and seeing weight come off helps to keep the negative emotions at bay.

Anorexia Nervosa

Some sufferers find that they are able to keep up their strict dieting. They are often high achievers in other areas. They begin to lose weight – sometimes dramatically fast, which is the most dangerous way. But although initially this may make them feel better, they are not actually dealing with the problems that were making them feel so low in the first place. Their weight can drop so low that they become very seriously ill. They may do other things to try to speed up weight loss including excessive exercise or taking diet pills or laxatives. Anorexia is a very serious condition. In fact more people die from anorexia than from any other mental health condition. Weight loss affects more than just the bits of their body they want to change, and can damage the heart and other organs. Sufferers can therefore feel and appear reasonably healthy whilst actually being seriously ill.

Binge Eating Disorder

Another group of sufferers start with the same desire to lose weight and set diets which are just as strict. However they find themselves unable to keep up the rigid control, and experience periods of time where they overeat on food that would usually be 'forbidden.' These can develop into 'binges' – when they eat huge quantities of food and feel a sense of having totally lost control. Following a binge they are overwhelmed with powerful negative emotions like guilt, and an absolute dread of gaining weight as a result of what they have eaten.

42

Bulimia Nervosa

A final group of sufferers find themselves filled with binge-induced disgust and then panic, developing another phase in their cycle of out-of-control eating. They start to do something in an attempt to avoid putting on weight because of what they have eaten in a binge. This 'purging' can involve making themselves sick, taking diet pills or laxatives, exercising or just fasting for days at a time after a binge. They believe that this stops them from gaining weight, but unfortunately what it does is to mean that swallowing food is no longer a 'point of no return'. Binges then tend to become even worse, and some sufferers find that they can eat a whole week's groceries in one, eat food that does not belong to them, or even eat food that isn't properly cooked or defrosted. Episodes of binging and purging alternate with times when they return to their strict diet, each time desperately meaning to regain control and stop what they are doing. However, they unwittingly set themselves up to fail, and eventually the cycle starts again. Their weight stays roughly normal and that, combined with their ability to hide what is going on, means that bulimia can go on for years without anyone knowing, and the secrecy and shame it carries with it can be devastating.

Get help fast

Whatever is going on, if you or someone you know is showing symptoms of an eating disorder, the golden rule is to get some help and support fast. Call one of the advice lines given below and talk it through. This can be done anonymously at first. It's vital that you talk to an expert and get some idea of how serious things are. It's also the first step to getting some help and treatment. Next, terrifying as it may feel, anyone with an eating disorder should be seen by their GP to check out their general health and make sure they are not at risk of serious complications. Even though you may feel fine your body might be struggling – get checked out! It's much better to make the decision to go and see your GP now whilst it is in your control than to wait until you are really ill and have no choice.

It IS possible to recover!

Although the media can paint a pretty gloomy picture of the future for sufferers with eating disorders the truth is that there is life after an eating disorder! It is possible to recover fully and to get past an eating disorder and go on to live a happy, confident and fulfilled life. Recovery is not about pretending to be ok and carrying on feeling rotten, though – it's about really working through the problems that triggered the eating disorder as well as improving eating patterns and getting out of the vicious cycles an eating disorder traps you within.

Worried about a friend? Some hints and tips for how to help:

- Eating disorders are not all about food! Remember that their eating is just a symptom of other things that they are struggling with and avoid the temptation to talk to them only about what they are or are not eating. Instead encourage them to talk about how they are feeling about other things. Give them space to talk and be prepared to listen.

- Avoid the temptation to nag! When someone is out of control it is a natural reaction to want to take control yourself. However this will not help them in the long run. Try to avoid becoming 'the food police', watching everything they do and do not eat. Instead be there for them and support them in changes they are trying to make without condemning them when things don't go so well.

- Help them to know they are more than just an eating disorder. When you are struggling against an eating disorder it can feel like it becomes all that you are. However, as their friend you know that they are about so much more. Make sure they know what it is about them that you love and the things about them you value. Help them to know that they do not have to earn your friendship but that you just like them for who they are.

- Help them to get help. Seeking treatment for an eating disorder may be the most difficult thing they have ever done in their life. You can help them to take this brave step by being there as they make the appointment with the GP, maybe going along with them or even sitting in the appointment with them. People suffering with eating disorders can feel like the whole world is against them, trying to take away their one coping strategy, and its important that they know you are on their side and want the best for them.

Getting more help

If you are worried about yourself or a friend, there are some specialist organisations you can contact for help and advice:

Anorexia & Bulimia Care   www.anorexiabulimiacare.co.uk

Anorexia & Bulimia Care is the UK national Christian charity supporting those who are struggling against eating disorders. Sufferer's helpline 01934 710679 or email suffererssupport@anorexiabulimiacare.co.uk; Parent/Carer's helpline 01934 710645 or email ache@anorexiabulimiacare.co.uk.

New ID   www.newid.info

New ID is a Christian course run within churches for people struggling with eating disorders, aimed at helping them reach freedom. For more info or to find a course near you see www.newid.info.

Mercy Ministries   www.mercyministries.co.uk

Mercy Ministries is a non profit organisation offering a free 6 month residential programme for young women who are suffering from eating disorders, self-harm, depression and the effects of abuse in all its forms. For more information see www.mercyministries.co.uk.

Sadness
I AM REALLY UNHAPPY

Homesick ↗ ↖

As we grow up, we expand the amount of time we stay away from our parents. A few hours at a party, a sleep-over, a weekend away with the Cub Scouts, travelling Europe with mates. However, aged 18 we are suddenly expected to be able to move to the other end of the country, meet a completely new set of friends and study harder than we have ever done before. Add to that the history for some of a broken home, the horrific embarrassment at the first disco or the poverty of no-loan-yet-itis and it is no wonder that many people become homesick at University.

Who it affects

Just because you have successfully left home before doesn't mean you won't get homesick. For some it happens in Fresher's Week, for other it takes longer and takes the form of preoccupation with home. For some there is just a massive anticlimax in coming to University – it isn't the idol it was set up to be, people are still stupid and sex isn't that good.

How people deal with it

Like our six characters on page 21-22, some cope by turning to alcohol or drugs, hoping that this will numb the pain. Does anyone really like drinking games? Others wear the mask of fashion, sport or academia, joining a 'set' or 'team'. The problem is that the infighting can be just as bad. For some it is so bad that they end up leaving University either temporarily or permanently. Some of these will try again or chose a new route, but some others will be permanently scarred.

What to do instead

1. A problem shared is a problem halved and in this case that happens to be true. Please TALK to someone, anyone.

2. Please allow yourself to feel sad, disappointed and let down at times. These emotions are not crimes and we all have them from time to time. This is one of those times, so trying to be Little Miss Happy will only make the emotions harder.

3. Pop home for a weekend if it is really tough, but try not to do this all the time and please make sure you come back!

4. Take a deep breath and consider whether you are doing the right course and are at the right university. It may not be to late to change modules or even subjects. For some, now is the time to quit and regroup and try again next year. Talk to your tutor, old school teacher, pastor, counselling service – they will all have come across these problems before.

How can you help?

The best people to help students are students. How can you help someone in your circle who is struggling without putting them on the spot. Try organising a dinner party for your flat or floor. Tell people when you are going to Asda or the Cinema and see if they want to come too. Invite them to church – weekends between lectures can be very long times…

Depression

Last week I got a phone call from one of my students. She was really worried about her fiancé. She'd started to think there was a problem when he got very lethargic towards the end of the academic year. He sat in the living room staring at the floor, and stopped going out with his mates. Whenever she asked him what was wrong, he became teary-eyed and vague. He talked about life being pointless and his future bleak. From his perspective he was weak and useless and wouldn't amount to anything. No matter what he did, he couldn't snap out of it. As she described the situation, it became clear that her fiancé was depressed, and we started to talk about how he might seek appropriate help from his GP. We feared that, without help, his hopeless state could lead him to harm himself [see p63 for more info on self-harm].

Depression is **not** sadness!

Depression is not the same as sadness or unhappiness. If you ask a depressed person if they feel sad, they may say yes, but quite often they'll say they feel numb, or nothing at all. If we feel sad we can usually be comforted. An arm around the shoulder, a kind word, a cup of tea, or a quick jog can be enough to draw us out of ourselves again. But, unlike sadness, depression can't be comforted. It feels like a trap. It feels like it'll last forever. That's why depressed people are notoriously resistant to exhortations to pull themselves together and get on with it. They can't do so easily- that's what depression is.

How do you know someone's depressed?

The first sign that someone you know is depressed will probably be a dip in mood that lasts longer than you would normally expect. They stop finding pleasure in the things they used to enjoy. Other signs to look out for could be:

- Eating more (or less) and putting on weight (or losing it)

- Sleeping too much or too little

- Problems concentrating, thinking and making decisions

- Loss of energy and constant tiredness, or alternatively, an inability to sit still

- Feeling worthless, guilty, or self-blaming

- Thinking about death and suicide attempts

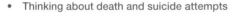

47

Where does depression come from?

As you can see, being depressed is no picnic. But in Western culture it's a relatively common experience for many people. It depends which survey you read, but some would estimate that, in the UK, up to half of women and a quarter of men are likely to have a depressive episode at some point in their lives. Further evidence suggests that our way of life, in the industrial developed world, creates the conditions in which depression thrives. A competitive success-driven culture encourages us to want more than we can have, leaving many of us dissatisfied and some of us depressed. There are also family traits – a combination of learned mood and genetics. There is therefore no single factor that causes depression, but rather a series of possible candidates that bring it about.

Is it a physical problem?

The most popular and widely publicised cause of depression is the 'biological' explanation. This is what people refer to when they talk about mental illness being an 'imbalance' of chemicals in the brain. And while this doesn't entirely explain all the features of depression, it is based on the fact that the brains of people who are depressed show a lower than average availability of certain neurotransmitters (the chemicals that communicate between brain cells), when compared to non-depressed people. The chief neurotransmitter involved is Serotonin, and many modern medications that target depression (such as Prozac [fluoxetine]or Seroxat [paroxetine]), act specifically to make more Serotonin available in the brain. Very often this will be the first treatment offered by a GP when a depressed person presents for the first time, and very often it will offer relief by lifting their mood to some extent. For some people that will be enough to get them out of their depressive slump, but most will need more than that to get back on their feet.

Is it a psychological problem?

Currently the most talked-about psychological understanding of depression is derived from an approach called Cognitive-Behavioural Therapy (CBT). In short, CBT suggests that depression is not just caused by chemical changes in the brain, but rather is the result of the way the person is thinking and behaving.

From an early age we develop rules and strategies for surviving in the world, particularly around what we need to do or be, in order to be loved or successful. We may not even know we've made these assumptions about life until they start to cause us problems. If, for example, our early experience taught us that we must always be top of the class, we may not know how much is riding on it until we find ourselves no longer in prime position. Similarly, if we believe that we need to be the most popular person around in order to be okay with ourselves, our mood will fluctuate with our social standing.

According to CBT, depression begins when the rules we have lived by (perhaps unknowingly) are broken or challenged. This is why depression can be triggered by seemingly insignificant events. Scoring an average pass in an exam, or falling out with a group of friends, may look trivial at face value, but if they violate rules on which we've based our self-esteem, they can be disastrous and lead to full-blown depression. The depression itself then acts as a trap. We look at how sad and incompetent we feel, and this makes us feel worse. It's a vicious cycle – we get depressed about being depressed.

Most psychological interventions for depression available on the NHS are based on CBT to some extent. There is also a variety of self-help materials available for people who feel able to work at it under their own steam. CBT teaches a series of psychological skills designed to combat low mood, such as: organising an enjoyable and productive day, challenging negative thought patterns, getting a good night's sleep, or learning to be assertive: all vital skills in shaking off depression and re-connecting with the world.

Is it a spiritual problem?

There is, however, an even more profound aspect to depression. As a clinician, one of the questions I regularly ask depressed patients is: at core, do you feel you are generally good and acceptable, or generally bad and unacceptable? People give a variety of answers. Overall, I've found that if we believe ourselves to be essentially bad, evil, worthless, rotten-to-the-core, then we have to find ways of dealing with the pain of thinking about ourselves in that way. We create rules by which to make ourselves acceptable, we work hard, we compete, we attract people and cling to them. We live with a giant question-mark hanging over us. Feeling bad at core, we do whatever we need to do to justify our existence.

The message of Christianity is that, through Jesus, we have been accepted at the deepest level. There's no longer a question-mark hanging over our right to be on the planet. We don't need to justify our existence, we've already been justified. That's our starting point. Most of us struggle to accept God's acceptance entirely, but when we're depressed we may struggle to accept it at all. The question for all of us (depressed or not) is therefore: what small steps can we take today to live more fully in the acceptance of God? And, if we struggle to believe we are accepted, how can we live 'as if' it is true?

Depression in most cases does not have a spiritual cause, but it is certainly a problem with a spiritual dimension and spiritual approaches can be of great help.

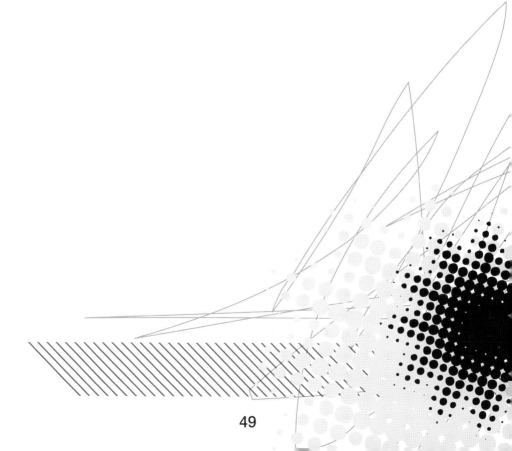

Anger

A friend of mine recently attended an anger management group run by the NHS. He's a nice guy, but every one knows he has a temper. When it starts brewing most of his friends try to stay clear. The wakeup call came when, after a couple of drinks, he argued with his girlfriend and nearly hit her. He loved her, and knew that if he didn't do something about his outbursts, the relationship wouldn't last. When he spoke to his GP about it, anger management was the first thing he recommended.

Colours of Anger

Some psychologists would say there are two kinds of anger: red anger and white anger.

RED ANGER is the appropriate human response to unfairness or frustration. It is a contact emotion. It aims to clarify, to re-establish relationship and tells people how we would prefer to be treated. It attempts to improve the world around us. If I put my hand over your mouth and attempted to stop you breathing, this is the kind of anger that would fight me off.

WHITE ANGER, on the other hand, is more like rage. It is destructive and often ineffective, and occurs when we feel helpless and don't know what else to do. It is a sign that we've given up hope of changing things for the better. This kind of anger can appear excessive and becomes a significant issue if accompanied by violence. In men, it may be a symptom of depression.

In itself, anger is not a problem, but it becomes one when it rages out of control.

Contents of Anger

Anger is a response of the whole person. It includes how we think, what we feel and what we do.

THOUGHTS. We become angry when we perceive something as being frustrating or unfair. Many of the thoughts that accompany anger concern the perceived injustice of the situation in which we find ourselves: the way other people have spoken or acted towards us.

FEELINGS. Anger is also a physical response. Our heart rate increases, our muscles (fists, jaw, eyebrows) tense ready for action, our face flushes, our back straightens. Sometimes we shake, narrow our eyes, or grind our teeth.

ACTIONS. Some angry behaviours, like raising our voice or repeating our point in an argument, can be functional ways of expressing our boundaries. Others, such as physical violence or verbal insults, potentially harm other people and therefore cause difficulty.

Control of Anger

People who struggle to manage their anger often describe acting aggressively before they've even noticed their temper flaring or had time to think about it. They only start thinking afterwards, and by then it's usually too late. The damage has been done and they may regret it. Most anger management programmes will recommend some of the following:

- Notice the signs that you are getting angry. Keep a look out for the clenched fists, the flushing of the face, the increased heart rate. These are the warning signs that you may be about to explode.

- Pause for a few moments. The old advice to count to ten before getting angry hasn't gone out of date. If you can notice your anger building, then you may like to take a moment to get out of the situation and calm down.

- Learn a variety of skills for getting what you want. If you resort to anger because you don't know what else to do, it may help to assert yourself and negotiate. As long as you have other options, you may not need to get mad.

- Start to channel anger productively. The most advanced anger management strategy is being able to get angry and think at the same time. While extreme anger stops us thinking, managed anger can be a great force for good, when combined with respect for other people.

51

Medication

Antidepressants

For people who are more severely depressed, taking medication may be a key part of getting better. This is because when you are so low, it is not possible to engage effectively with 'talking treatments' and God may seem so far off that you are not able to lean on Him. Medication is NOT typically offered for more mild forms of depression, and your GP should not be reaching for the prescription pad as an alternative to helping you get to see a counsellor or therapist.

Scientists think that in depression there is a lack of a certain chemical – serotonin [sometimes called 5-HT]. This causes the brain to process in a depressive way. Personally, we believe that this lack is caused by being depressed and stressed for a while rather than this being the primary root of depression – there is a slight genetic component in depression, but events in our upbringing and lives are the main factors. Antidepressants [of which there are about ten different types which all act in slightly different ways] act in the main by increasing the serotonin levels in our brains. The side effects are caused either by increasing serotonin levels in unhelpful areas or by affecting the levels of other chemicals – most side effects are mild, reversible and transient.

However, antidepressants are not 'happy pills' either. They will not make you magically feel fantastic – they are designed to remove the symptoms of depression and they work best in people who have lots of bodily symptoms like weight loss, tiredness or poor sleep. They do not give you self-esteem and do not improve your personality. Likewise, if the causes of depression are still unaddressed, they may not help with severe depression at all.

Antidepressants should be taken for an initial six-week period to see if they work [set goals for them: e.g., sleep, energy levels, libido] and, if they do work, they should be continued for at least another six months. Do NOT be tempted to stop them early. They are not addictive like heroin or alcohol, but should be stopped slowly under medical supervision – like any medicine.

Antidepressants and Christians

Clinical Depression is an illness and so it is perfectly possible for a Christian to be depressed in exactly the same way as it is possible for you to break your leg. Similarly, though God does heal some physical illnesses with miracles, most will also get better with modern medicine. Why should antidepressants be any different? Depression will affect your faith and how you relate to others and to your church, but so will a chronic physical illness. It doesn't mean your faith is weak or that you have committed some horrible sin. In fact, if you are wondering if you have committed some "unforgivable sin" the chances are that you haven't!

Antidepressants may act on the brain, but so do paracetamol and antiepileptic medication. They may have side-effects, but so does chemotherapy and untreated depression isn't so nice either. They can however be over-relied upon and the Christian is called to take a holisitic approach to life – using medication where indicated, using psychology where helpful, sorting out practical problems when needed and keeping the faith at all times.

Other psychiatric medications

The other main groups of psychiatric medications are below – but this is not an exhaustive list. The same principles apply to them all. Please see the pages in this booklet about more serious forms of mental illness [which are more biological in nature] like schizophrenia on page 72.

ANTIPSYCHOTIC MEDICATION
prescribed for Schizophrenia and other psychotic illnesses

STIMULANTS
prescribed for Attention Deficit and Hyperactivity Disorder

MOOD STABILISERS
prescribed for Bipolar Affective Disorder and other manic illnesses

BENZODIAZEPINES
prescribed short term for sedation and anxiety [should not be taken long term as they are addictive and tolerance develops]

Substance Misuse
ANYTHING CAN BE ADDICTIVE

Boozing

Alcohol is the ultimate socially acceptable drug. For millennia, mankind has been fermenting almost anything that grows [and some things that walk!]. Even in countries and cultures that are 'dry', there is a lot of it about. Prohibitions don't seem to be the answer. In all of these situations, there have been abuses and misery for many.

Alcohol is not heroin, so it can seem safe, and there are obviously a number of significant differences – see page 58 for a bit more on heroin. One of the key ones is that most people who take heroin will end up with problems, whereas most people who drink will not. It seems safe, and this is its downfall, because it will be far from safe for a significant majority. Scotland, where I live, has the highest drinking levels in Europe – oh, and also the highest rate of alcohol related brain damage. Here are some numbers:

- We drank the equivalent of 12 litres of pure alcohol per year per person

- 60% of drinkers consume more than the recommended amount – defined as HARMFUL drinking

- 13% of men have signs of not being able to control their intake – defined as PROBLEM drinking

- 777 per 100000 population had an alcohol-related admission to hospital

But it can't be that bad, can it? A few drinks here, a tipple there… And it does seem unfair that many people seem to get away with drinking sociably and with control – it can relax us and it goes well with food. I enjoy few things more than a nice glass of wine, but I also know that I can drink too much and that it makes me do things that can be stupid. It concerns me that one day it might take control.

Why do some people have problems?

There are two schools of thought. Alcoholics Anonymous believe that whilst some can drink safely there is a type of person they call an 'alcoholic' who cannot drink safely – not now and not ever. The other school says that there is no line in the sand but that alcohol draws you in slowly and inexorably. It doesn't really matter which you believe as the results are the same – quite a number of people who seem to start well go on to have MAJOR problems with alcohol, and if they do get clean they would be fools to drink again.

We don't know that much about why some people have problems with alcohol. Drinking to cover up emotional pain is a big reason – and if this is the case the person has to get help for their mental health at the same time as their addiction – though this can be hard if they binge drink rather than do the hard work of therapy, so often the drink has to be tackled first. Others drink because their parents drank and they just copied. More still seem to have a genetic predisposition to drink [and will remain at risk even if adopted], but this still needs to be activated.

Many start behind the bike sheds and continue in the alcohol-fuelled social life of University. Have you ever thought how hard it would be never to drink, or to socialise without going to a bar? So most students drink, and most drink too much from time to time. Some get into deeper trouble.

Going steady or on the wagon?

There are two ways to tackle harmful or problem drinking – to cut it out completely or to cut it down to a more sensible level. There is no right or wrong method, but the individual has to decide. Cutting down the drinking cuts down the harm almost immediately, and if you can still drink at this level then that is easiest socially. However, you need to keep close accountability with someone you trust and whom you will obey – if it starts to creep up again, you really need to consider Option Two.

Which is total abstinence. Not for any moral or religious reason, but for your health and sanity – literally. If you have a major problem with drink, this is the best way to go. You can tell yourself it is just for a few months, but my advice would be to make it for good. It IS possible to socialise without alcohol. It IS possible to find appetising alternatives to alcoholic drinks.

Know your limits

Increasingly, bars and supermarkets are marking the number of units as well as the percentage alcohol. But for those of you who need reminding…

- For a 100cl bottle at 12%, this is 12 units. A typical bottle is 75cl, which is 8 units.

- Large glass of red wine = 3 units

- Pint of beer = 2 to 3 units

- Bottle of spirits = 30 units. Typical unmeasured shot = 2 units

- Legal Driving Limit = 80mg per 100ml blood. Typical first fine £400, max £5000 + 6 months in prison and unlimited duration ban

For men, three to four units per day is considered a safe amount and for women it is no more than two to three units per day.

Self Assessment

Questionnaires are commonly used by health care professionals to evaluate levels of drinking. The CAGE questionnaire is most simple – if you say YES to more than 2 questions, you are a problem drinking [see above].

1. Have you ever felt you should cut down on your drinking?

2. Have people annoyed you by criticising your drinking?

3. Have you ever felt bad or guilty about your drinking?

4. Have you ever had a drink first thing in the morning to steady your nerves or get rid of a hangover (eye-opener)?

The AUDIT questionnaire can be found easily on the internet and is a more sensitive tool to detect HARMFUL drinking – the stage that comes before you have the start of a physical addiction.

 Calculate your alcohol intake at
www.drinkaware.co.uk/tips-and-tools/drink-diary

Getting more help

On campus – talk to your student counselling service – see page 91 for more info.

Off campus, there are many people you could talk to and your GP is a good place to start, but here are a few recommended websites and organisations:

ALCOHOLICS ANONYMOUS – www.alcoholics-anonymous.org.uk | 0845 7697555

ALCOHOL CONCERN - www.alcoholconcern.org.uk

DRINK AWARE – www.drinkaware.co.uk

Drugged Up

There are many addictive substances apart from alcohol and they have been used in every culture for centuries. Caffeine is one good example. However, whilst most people can drink coffee sensibly, some can become addicted – and this is true of the other substances too

Drug Classifications

These are meant to reflect the risk of addiction and the risk of damage, with Class A drugs being the most dangerous. Governments change classifications for political as well as scientific reasons, but they are still a good place to start. There are also different criminal penalties at each level. The table below is correct as of November 2009 but may change.

		Possession	Dealing
Class A	Ecstasy, LSD, heroin, cocaine, crack, magic mushrooms, amphetamines (if prepared for injection).	Up to seven years in prison or an unlimited fine or both.	Up to life in prison or an unlimited fine or both.
Class B	Amphetamines, Cannabis, Methylphenidate (Ritalin), Pholcodine.	Up to five years in prison or an unlimited fine or both.	Up to 14 years in prison or an unlimited fine or both.
Class C	Tranquilisers, some painkillers, Gamma hydroxybutyrate (GHB), Ketamine.	Up to two years in prison or an unlimited fine or both.	Up to 14 years in prison or an unlimited fine or both.

How big a problem is this?

The sentences above seem strict and there is criticism that they are never applied. After all, don't people smoke cannabis in Holland all the time?

But this attitude is a misunderstanding of the problem. Firstly, the cannabis you get in Holland is much weaker and contains less active 'THC' so causes less mind alteration. Secondly, the Europeans are much better than the Brits in using drugs [and alcohol] in moderation. Thirdly, though many students use cannabis without any problems, there is a significant minority who have major problems with addiction and the secondary consequences for friendships, debt and studying. Cannabis destroys degrees.

Getting more help

Most universities recognize addictions [alongside sexual health and mental health] as one of their top three challenges, so there should be help available. Start at

THE STUDENTS' UNION – look for posters, fliers, phone numbers

STUDENT SERVICES AND THE COUNSELLING SERVICE – they may point you to other local addiction services if the problem is severe, but they are a good place to start and will also help with any underlying problems [see page 46 for some examples] that may have led to the substance misuse in the first place.

LOCAL NHS ADDICTION SERVICES – ask your GP or look on the local NHS website via www.nhs.uk

Talk to Frank – Confidential advice, support and referral. www.talktofrank.com, 0800 77 66 00, frank@talktofrank.com Text 82111

CHRISTIAN MINISTRIES specialising in freedom from addiction: www.walkingfree. org, www.teenchallenge.org.uk

The 12 ½ Steps

Alcoholics Anonymous is one of the original self-help movements. They describe '12 steps' to help you deal with alcohol. Though most of you reading this book won't be alcohol dependant, we have put them in here as they were organically based on what it means to be a Christian – we have 'translated them' back into Christian terminology in the square brackets. What step are you on – in both your attitude to addictions and your journey with God?

Howard Astin, pastor of a church in Bradford where many of the congregation come from backgrounds of addiction, has added an extra half-step which he thinks is makes them even more effective. This extra half-step also ties in better with the idea that though we have done things wrong, a large component of mental distress comes from the wrongs others have done to us – such as abuse for example.

Book Recommendation
The Twelve and a Half Steps to Spiritual Health
Howard Astin, Monarch Books, ISBN: 978-1854245793, £8.00 ish

The steps

1. We admitted we were powerless over alcohol [sin] - that our lives had become unmanageable.

2. We came to believe that a Power greater than ourselves could restore us to sanity.

3. We made a decision to turn our will and our lives over to the care of God as we understood Him.

4. We made a searching and fearless moral inventory of ourselves.

5. We admitted to God, to ourselves, and to another human being the exact nature of our wrongs [some people in AA use the Sermon on the Mount from Matthew chapter 5 as a structure for this].
   a. THE EXTRA HALF STEP - We admitted to God, to ourselves, and to another human being the exact nature of the wrongs done to us.

6. We were entirely ready to have God remove all these defects of character.

7. We humbly asked Him to remove our shortcomings.

8. We made a list of all persons we had harmed, and became willing to make amends to them all.

9. We made direct amends to such people wherever possible, except when to do so would injure them or others.

10. We continued to take personal inventory and when we were wrong promptly admitted it.

11. We sought through prayer and meditation to improve our conscious contact with God as we understood Him, praying only for knowledge of His will for us and the power to carry that out.

12. Having had a spiritual awakening as the result of these steps, we tried to carry this message to alcoholics [all those in need of the good news of Jesus], and to practice these principles in all our affairs.

Book Recommendation
Alcoholics Anonymous – The Big Book [4th Edition]
AA Worldwide, Hazelden, ISBN: 978-1893007161, £8.50 ish

Other Traps

The problem with addictions is that they work – we tend to get addicted to things that make us feel good, for a while at least… It's not just drugs and alcohol – people can have addictions to gambling, sun bathing, sport, food, tattoos. What rocks your boat? What do you use to cover up your inadequacies? As Gok would say, do you look good naked?

Fig Leaves and Nakedness

Addictions make us think we have covered up our nakedness. We can hide behind the prestigious job, the extreme snow-board dude look, the fake-bake tan. They superficially make us happy because they get us places socially [from one point of view] and have a certain buzz about them. They are risky, but that is half the fun. However, they fail to ultimately satisfy. The tan wrinkles, the dude ages, the job sucks.

The Bible says of fig leaves and our other attempts at weaving coverings that 'their cobwebs are useless for clothing; they cannot cover themselves with what they have made' [Isaiah 59v9]. They always fail if you give them enough time. The problem is that when they do fail, we can rail against God saying he doesn't love us and life hurts, whereas in fact the problem is that we are naked because WE rejected HIS love back in the Garden of Eden.

The answer to nakedness is not cobwebs – flimsy pursuits that we humans weave to make us feel good – but clothing from the Almighty himself. He started with the clothing he made from skins in the Garden for Adam and Eve. It continues today – we are 'clothed with Christ', given 'robes of white', 'covered by His love'. Gok is right to a point – we are beautiful just the way we are, because when we realise who we are we realise we are children of God. No need for cover up. No need for things to hide the pain. No need for masks.

Leaf by Leaf

Here are some of the other common non-drug addictions and some tips to help with them. However, the ultimate answer is finding a real purpose in life.

SPORT: Can you lose gracefully? Can you take a week or two off at the end of the season? Do you have friends down the gym? Answer: spend some time playing with young children as they know how to have real fun.

TANNING: Do you continue to tan despite evidence of harm? Have other people started making comments? Answer: get a skin check to see if you have early cancerous signs – this should be a wake up call. Give twenty pounds to a friend every time you get a tan.

WORKAHOLISM: OK you may be a student now, but most students work, and we hope that a job is just around the corner! Will you spend more than you earn? When did you last take a holiday? Do you ever talk about anything else apart from your job/degree? Do you have friends outside your work/course? Answer: join an unrelated sports team, take a long enough holiday to get really away and turn the blackberry off – you might even have fun and work may even manage without you.

GAMBLING: have you lost more than you have won? Do you gamble in secret or online? Do you have 'friends' who are only around when you win? Answer: get rid of the internet connection – you can't afford it. Talk to Gamblers Anonymous – **www.gamblersanonymous.org.uk.**

Self-harm
WHEN YOU START TO HURT YOURSELF

Let's Talk ↗ ↖

This section deals with some stuff that can be difficult to talk about – when painful feelings and emotions lead people to struggle with thoughts – or with actual actions - of hurting themselves in one way or another. Although this might be a tricky subject, it's really important that we think and talk about this – feelings like this are increasingly common. In fact hundreds of thousands of hospital admissions every year are because someone has deliberately hurt themselves – and the number of young people in particular being treated in hospital for self-inflicted wounds/illnesses is increasing. One charity carried out a survey that found 1/3 of girls aged 11-19 said they had harmed themselves and nearly half of teenagers admit to having had suicidal thoughts at least once. We know that once the pressures of university life kick in these feelings don't just vanish – and many students struggle with feelings of self-hatred and episodes of self-harm.

Feelings this extreme are nothing to be ashamed or guilty about – nor do they mean that you are crazy. They are simply a sign that you are under a lot of pressure and that you need some help. They are, however, a serious sign that something needs to change – so don't ignore them. They are triggered by emotions and situations that may feel out of control, overwhelming or frightening. Sometimes they may be linked with specific memories or events. It can be tempting to try to put those moments behind you when you walk out of the door, and to pretend that everything is ok. The vast majority of people who do self-harm wish that they did not, and most feel very ashamed of what they do and keep it secret even from those who care most about them. But not talking about it doesn't make self-harm go away – in fact what it does is push it underground. This just makes things worse because then you have to lie, hide or cover up the reality of what is going on instead of bringing it out into the open and getting help.

Keep talking ...

There is a common misconception that talking about issues like these can make things worse – even put ideas in people's minds. This really isn't true! Self-harm is such a common issue now that most people are well aware of it already. The only impact not talking about it has is to magnify the feelings of shame and self-hatred people are already experiencing. If we do not talk openly – and with real wisdom – about these issues then we cannot support people and help them to work through them to a place of real recovery. Like it or not, we live in a society where many people right now are facing difficult and extreme emotions, or events and situations that they don't know how to handle. We know that humans under this kind of pressure sometimes react by experiencing thoughts of ending their own lives as they desperately seek relief and a way out of what they are going through. The bible itself has its own examples of this. Look at Elijah who, after an incredibly stressful few days, ran away and called out to God begging him to take his life (1 Kings 19:4). Even Paul, thrown into jail and facing an unknown future, struggled with the desire to have reached the end of his life, admitting "I desire to depart and be with Christ, which is better by far" (Phil 1:23).

Some Christians in particular struggle with these issues, and the reactions they experience within the church are no less powerful than outside. Many sufferers have had bad experiences of things that often well-meaning people have said and done. But God does not condemn people who have felt this way and neither should we. It is vital that we talk about the challenges we're facing – and together help people work towards real recovery and the kind of genuine transformation that Jesus can bring.

64

Self-harm

Roots and Reasons

There are many actions people undertake which can result in harm. These may include extreme sports, drinking too much, taking drugs, unprotected sex, driving at speed, and so on. These actions may be reckless or intentional and could well result in harm to the individual in the short term or long term, yet rarely is the plan to cause oneself-harm; harm arises as a side effect of the experience or thrill.

Reckless behaviour may be dangerous, but is not of itself "self-harm". So what is self-harm?

Defining Self-harm

- Self-harm is a **deliberate and intended action** designed to cause harm to your own self. This usually takes the form of a physical self injury although can include emotional/psychological consequences.

- Self-harm is **not an act of attempted suicide**; there is no intention to kill oneself, although certain forms of self-harm could unintentionally result in death. It is therefore not nihilistic – an attempt to end life

- Self-harm is usually **not "just attention seeking**." It is commonly done in private, on parts of the body, which can be covered by clothing. It is a personal act and not a public one, and often only comes to light by accident or if the individual panics about the depth of the cut or recognises they need help.

Who self-harms?

- Both men and women, although more women than men

- Any age group, although most think of it as linked to the teens and twenties with people coping with the angst of youth

- 1 in 10 teenagers self-harm. Among young people, the ratio of female to male is 3:1

- The UK has the highest recorded self-harm rate in Europe

Why does a person start to self-harm?

Many people stumble into self-harming. Some might act initially out of anger or frustration, and hit something or cut themselves to express their pain, and, unexpectedly, when they cause injury they realise that they strangely feel better inside. Some may hear about self-harming from others and copy it. Others may try to cut their wrists as part of a suicide attempt, but by cutting themselves they realise that they can get relief. Some are drawn to self-harm through stress (school work is a major trigger for some teenagers). Yet others may find that self-harm gives them a sense of control over something in their lives (which are usually controlled by events or others). Self-harm can make "real" the emotional pain an individual cannot express, giving it an outlet.

Understanding Self-harm

Self-harm is still somewhat of a taboo subject. Someone new to the subject can feel horror and shock, and be disturbed by the thoughts of self injury and the gory nature of the actions involved. They may well be bewildered as to why anyone would want to deliberately cause themselves hurt, pain and injury. These responses can lead to avoidance. However, when you know someone who is self-harming then all of this is supplemented with a desire to help, to support, to come to the rescue, to care. The first task is not any of these. It has to be "to learn to understand."

Self-harm is not an attempt to end life but a means to live. It is a learnt coping mechanism that gives the individual a chance to relieve internal tension, pressure or distress and live their life.

Self-harm is not a mental illness. It is an unhealthy coping mechanism associated with powerful emotions, but is not of itself an illness. Some self-harmers hide the activity from others as they are frightened that they are "mad." It can be linked to disassociation – a psychological state where an individual separates themselves from things around them, often as a way to cope with overwhelming distress.

Self-harm usually occurs as self-inflicted injury such as cutting, stabbing, burning, hitting hard objects, rubbing, scratching, or scraping. It may also include swallowing foreign objects. The usual feature is that the action causes pain, injury to the skin, and often bleeding.

Self-harm is a way to cope with inner feelings If an individual feels intense hurt, frustration, tension, pain or anger inside and they find it hard to cope with these feelings, then instead of taking them out on someone else or just bottling them up they may look to self-harming.

Self-harm can be a ritual of self-punishment. Some individuals feel a need to inflict punishment on themselves; they feel that they have done something wrong or have had guilt put upon them and there is a need for retribution, and they are the ones to carry out the sentence on themselves. An extension of this involves the symbolism of blood letting which is seen as a purging or cleansing act releasing any evil from within, letting out the poison or pain inside.

Self-harm deflects inner distress. Causing physical pain can deflect a person's attention from their inner pain, albeit for a limited period of time. For a while it can feel easier to cope with the physical pain instead of the emotional or psychological. The pain can reassure the individual as it reinforces that they are real, still have feelings, that they are alive.

Self-harm releases chemical defences in the body. When "attacked" the body goes into defence/self protection mode. There is a complex internal physical response to the injury. This response involves powerful chemicals produced by the body called **endorphins**. These work to enable the person to cope with their injury by giving a natural tranquilising effect to relieve the pain, thereby giving relief to both physical and emotional pain, and causing a calming effect on the person. The endorphins also lift the mood, giving a high to enable the "fight or flight" response with a sense of "buzz" or energising effect. The high has been compared with that of certain illicit drugs and even sex. As with other highs, once experienced there is a tendency to want to experience the effect again. This leads to the temptation to repeat the self-harm when the internal emotional tension and pressure begin to build again.

Self-harm is addictive. As can be seen, above, the release of endorphins can easily become addictive as the individual seeks to revisit the tranquilising effect and natural high they have achieved in the past. The sense of physical pain deflecting an emotional load is also powerfully addictive. A third type of dependency may arise from the emotional and caring responses of others to the person when they self-harm.

Self-harm Cycles are hard to break. The natural effect caused by the endorphins complicates the issue. A person may start to self-harm because of emotional and psychological feelings inside which they express in the self-injury. To bring help in the long term these root causes need to be addressed along with the dependency on the effect of the endorphins, and other complicating behavioural habits.

Dangerous yet attractive

Self-harm is an abnormal coping mechanism that should never be encouraged and it is dangerous to the individual. It tends to escalate in the same way as other addictive behaviours, adding to the physical risk of major harm to the body, infection, anaemia, etc. Others may be tempted to copycat the behaviours out of need or curiosity, especially if encouraged to try out self-harm by someone who thinks it is helping them. Those in emotional distress end up with two problems instead of one: inner turmoil coupled with addiction. Self-harm cycles need to be replaced by healthier coping strategies.

Managing Self-harm

Responding to an incident of self-harm. The response must be calm, matter of fact and practical. Most importantly, ensure the injuries are cleaned and treated. This may mean going to Accident and Emergency. Minor injuries can be dressed at home. Do not panic. This calm approach is the best way to keep the individual physically safe and well, but also reduces the risk of any emotional response feeding their desire to self-harm. A secondary emotional gain can be psychologically addictive.

Responding day to day. The person needs to be "noticed" and cared for all the time, not just when they self-harm. There should be no blame and no shame. They need opportunities to talk, and to learn how people express and deal with emotions in safer ways. Encourage the person to seek expert help. Be there for them, but do not allow them to become over dependent. They need to be helped by professionals. Seek advice and support for yourself if you are supporting someone who self-harms.

Do not stifle self-harm. If the underlying causes are not addressed, making an individual stop self-harming may lead to even more destructive activities to relieve their unresolved emotions. These might include alcohol or drug abuse, promiscuity, or actual suicide attempts.

Practical alternatives for the self-harming individual. There are activities that can be used as an alternative to self-harming to break the habit/dependence. These include:

- Pinging an elastic band to inflict pain without cutting the skin

- Going through the motion with a blunt blade without breaking the skin

- Putting ice on the arm

- Drawing red lines on the arm (feeling of the ball point plus visual effect)

- Releasing endorphins through exercise, sex, eating hot foods like chilli and curry or intense mints

- Hot (not too hot) or cold shower

- Doing something enjoyable as a distraction

- Writing out feelings

- Punching and shouting into a pillow

Seeking help

Although these strategies may work in the short term, there is still a need to get expert help: to talk to someone, to face the problems, and deal with the root. The person needs help to stop but this cannot be done without support. The distress inside is like a pressure cooker on boil where both the heat needs to be turned off **and** the weight or burden released.

Medical help should be sought to reduce the effects of scarring which could be upsetting to the individual years after ceasing to self-harm.

Suicide

Suicide is the ultimate act, the final sanction and the most extreme method of control. But it is also one of the saddest things there is, both for the person and for the people they leave behind. Thankfully, the numbers of students who die by suicide is very small indeed. But is does happen. This section looks at some of the history, prejudices and how you can make a difference.

Silence and Stigma

Like many forms of mental health problem, people who are planning suicide rarely talk about it openly. This is in part because they do not want to be stopped, but it is also because they are worried they will face misunderstanding and ridicule. People can be especially angry, blaming the person for 'leaving them' and children in particular can find it very hard.

Yet for the person themselves, the suicide will have been a rational act. From where they were, in the dark, dark place they will have been in, suicide will have seemed the only and last option and the best way to help those around them – who they often believe they have been a burden to.

Luckily, many more people are talking about suicide today and talking about it does NOT make the person more likely to carry it out. In fact it can be a huge relief to be able to talk about these feelings they thought were forbidden and taboo.

Unhelpful History

Many people still think that suicide is a crime and indeed it was till 1961, but not for the reasons you'd think. The problems started in about 300-400 AD just after the time when lots of Christians were being martyred and persecuted. An idea had got around that it was somehow more holy to die as a martyr and you would get a better place in heaven. So, when the persecutions stopped, some Christians engineered martyrdom by taunting Roman officials until they were beheaded. Not surprisingly church officials were not keen on this and tried various forms of warning and prohibition but none were effective.

They had to resort to threatening would-be pseudo-martyrs with excommunication [being told they were no longer forgiven by God] and banning them from being buried in consecrated ground [meaning they would not go to heaven according to the thinking of the time]. This was incorporated into the Catholic catechism as a 'mortal sin' and into British Law meaning suicide was illegal. Only in 1961 was this changed, meaning relatives could claim life insurance and suicide victims could be buried in cemeteries. Only in the 1990s did the Catholics amended their catechism to allow people who had died by suicide to be excused a mortal sin if this was for mental health reasons. Is it any wonder people are fearful of suicide and all it means?

Suicide in the Bible

Many people wonder if suicide is a sin because they think it is condemned in the Bible. Below are the seven times people explicitly take their own lives in the Bible

- Abimelech (Judges 9:52-54) - Abimelech had an identity crisis

- Samson (Judges 16:25-30) - Samson died for a cause he believed in and for revenge

- Saul (1 Samuel 31:4) - Stressed out, unable to live up to certain expectations; felt rejected and a failure

- Saul's armour-bearer (1 Samuel 31:5) - Impulse, he wanted to die with his boss

- Ahithophel (2 Samuel 17:23) - Ahithophel was bitter because his advice was not followed

- Zimri (1 Kings 16:15-20) - Rebellion; Zimri had a problem with authority

- Judas (Matthew 27:3-5) - Depressed, Judas felt trapped by materialism and guilt

You may know some of these as the names of good guys and bad guys and hence form opinions. But why not read the texts themselves – you will find that the Bible is surprisingly quiet on the morals of what they did. Perhaps we should be too until we know better.

Severe Mental Illness
TIME TO ACT NOW!

Psychosis ⬀ ⬋

Because I work as a Psychiatrist, some people think that a trip to see me is not complete without the archetypal question, "Do you hear voices". However, though I do usually cover this at some point, that question itself is next to useless.

Some people will run a mile – especially if they actually suffer from something like OCD [page 38] and just FEAR they are going mad. Others will have voices which for them are quite normal – about 1% of the UK population chronically hear voices and are not ill at all. And the group who you might think I am interested in (those with Schizophrenia) do not all hear voices and (as a diagnostician) I am interested in far more than just hearing a voice.

Causes for Voice Hearing

NORMALITY: Hearing voices or complex noises can be a normal experience and people live otherwise healthy lives. If it gets bad, the Hearing Voices Network **(www.hearing-voices. org)** have a helpful website with links to books and self-help groups all around the country. This resource can also be useful for some of the people who hear voices for the reasons listed below.

SPLIT-MIND: The literal meaning of the word schizophrenia is 'split brain' but this is a misnomer – this is not what is happening in schizophrenia. But there are people whose mind is 'split' who hear voices. This may have occurred as a result of awful trauma when young such as sexual abuse – and our natural defence mechanism is to split off that awful memory into a hidden part of the brain. But humans don't do well with hidden bits, and it tries to get out – some times as flashbacks, but sometimes as the voice of the abuser saying nasty things like "You are dirty/ horrible/useless."

LOW SELF-ESTEEM: When our mood is chronically lowered, not typically due to depression which is episodic, but due to low self-worth; we can begin to hear a voice that resonates with our mood. It is more like an audible conscious stream of negative and critical comments: "You are useless. You are fat. I can see why no-one wants to be your friend…"

SUBSTANCE MISUSE: If you use alcohol heavily, or other street drugs like amphetamines that stimulate dopamine [see below] you will be likely to hear voices. In chronic alcohol use, the voice is similar to in low self-esteem above. In amphetamine intoxication it can be anything from hearing police sirens to thinking you are in space and 'Ground Control' is trying to reach you…

SEVERE MENTAL ILLNESS: People with schizophrenia will experience all kinds of voices. General paranoia is common, but psychiatrists are particularly interested in three types of voice: Two or more people talking about you, a voice commenting on your actions, hearing your own thoughts read out aloud. These voices are strongly suggesting of schizophrenia rather than other causes. Voices are also sometimes heard in other severe mental illnesses such as bipolar affective disorder, advanced dementia or very severe depression.

Schizophrenia

Though a fairly uncommon cause of hearing voices, this is worth an extra mention due to the fact that people know almost nothing about it – yet think they know enough to pass judgement. It is a very severe mental illness and needs urgent management by a psychiatrist supported by a well-equipped team. You will probably be offered anti-psychotic medication (see page 53), as an abnormality of brain chemistry [specifically dopamine transmission] in the frontal and temporal lobes is thought to be a key feature. However, it is never just about medication and should ALWAYS be accompanied by some kind of support (according to how much you need), some kind of talking therapy (to reduce the anxiety associated with the symptoms) and a crisis plan (of things to do if symptoms worsen). Some people may need to come into hospital for a while.

However, it is not something to be afraid of. Sadly, people have a negative image of schizophrenia – largely thanks to films like 'One flew over the cuckoo's nest' and 'Me, myself and Irene'. The first is woefully out of date and even then inaccurate, the second is about multiple personality disorder and psychopathy – things completely unrelated to schizophrenia even if Jim Carey doesn't know this. Also, Christians can need reminding that Schizophrenia is NOT demon possession – most of the cases of demon possession in the Bible are completely unlike Schizophrenia and even the 'Gerasene Demoniac' in Mark 5 is pretty far off the mark. For a more complete discussion on this topic, look at the Mind and Soul website **(www. mindandsoul.info)** and search for 'demon'.

Schizophrenia affects 1 % of the population at some point in their lives and treatment can last for several years. This means that there are lots of people on treatment and you would never know – anymore that you could tell a person with diabetes was on insulin. People with Schizophrenia (and please lets call them this, not 'schizophrenics' or 'nutters') are more likely to get hit that hit you – they are not typically violent, especially when well. In fact, in my experience, I have typically found them to be amazing and resourceful people who have to live with a severe illness that affects something very close to their core. Perhaps you or I would do well to meditate on this before we jump to any conclusions.

Cannabis and Schizophrenia

It is well known that smoking too much grass can make you a bit edgy – even paranoid. But this typically settles. Opinion is divided as to whether heavy use will actually CAUSE schizophrenia. Statistically, there is a dose-related correlation between use and later Schizophrenia. However, it could be that it just brought to the fore something that was going to develop anyway. Cannabis is also used by some people to take the edge of voices in the short-term. However, unfortunately it tends to make voices worse in the long term. It can also be a 'gateway' to other more serious drugs like amphetamines and heroin. See page 58 for more about drugs.

Students and Schizophrenia

The peak age of onset for Schizophrenia is in the early twenties so it may well develop at University. It is triggered (though not caused) by stress, so can particularly emerge in Freshers' Week – most Universities will see several new cases each September. It may also emerge more slowly as a person struggles to adapt to the new environment.

A 'typical' person developing Schizophrenia (and this is only typical) may have given some warning signs early on such as being uncharacteristically rigid in their thinking or having a few 'BLIPS' (brief limited intermittent psychotic symptoms) of voices or paranoia that last for a few days then back to normal. There may well be a close family member with the illness. They may be using drugs, not as a cause for the problem, but to help them cope with symptoms. They will most likely be self-isolating and you will see their life begin to deteriorate on a number of levels (appearance, work, hygiene) not just in what they say and think.

This is one of the situations where you should encourage the person to seek help themselves but, if they will not, you may want to go over their head as early treatment is more effective and can help prevent a severe breakdown later. See page 75 for ideas on how to help someone who does not want to be helped.

More information

Hearing Voices Network – www.hearing-voices.org, 0845 122 8641

Royal College of Psychiatrists Leaflets - www.rcpsych.ac.uk/mentalhealthinfo.aspx

Mind (mental health charity) – www.mind.org, 0845 766 0163

NHS info and video - www.nhs.uk/conditions/psychosis

More Information

Hearing Voices Network – www.hearing-voices.org, 0845 122 8641
Royal College of Psychiatrists Leaflets - www.rcpsych.ac.uk/mentalhealthinfo.aspx
Mind (mental health charity) – www.mind.org, 0845 766 0163
NHS info and video - www.nhs.uk/conditions/psychosis

Getting Urgent Help ↗ ↖

This page tells you where to go for help in a hurry. Please do use these numbers if you are in a crisis – remember these services are here for times like this. They want to help.

Who	How	
Your GP	Ring up and ask for an urgent appointment – they should have someone you can see that day even if it is not your usual GP.	
NHS Direct [England and Wales]	24 hour advice for people in England and Wales 0845 4567 www.nhs24.com	**NHS Direct**
NHS 24 [for Scotland]	24 hour advice for people in Scotland 0845 242424 www.nhs24.com	**NHS 24**
Your local A&E / Casualty / ER	These are open 24 hours a day and you can just walk in if it is a genuine emergency. Remember not all hospitals have an A&E department. Look for the Red Sign	**H A & E**
Call 999	In a real emergency when you cannot get to the hospital, you can call 999 from any phone and ask for an Ambulance. Don't forget this may need a 9 or other digit in front of it if you are in a Hall of Residence	
The Samaritans	A confidential phone line you can call if you are feeling suicidal 0845 909090 www.samaritans.org jo@samaritans.org	**SAMARITANS**

What if someone doesn't want to be helped?

First try to encourage them to get help. Explain that these services exist exactly for situations like this. Explain to them that they are making you feel uncomfortable and would they mind getting help to set your fears to rest.

If you really feel you have to, this may be a time to break confidence – especially if you feel the situation is life threatening. They may not like it at the time, but if it was a genuine emergency, most people will forgive you later. Loyalty is not the same as watching someone harm themselves – a true friend will get help.

You can either phone one of these numbers for advice in an immediate emergency, or if it is less immediate talk to someone at the University – see page 91 for some ideas.

High Society
PEOPLE, SEX, NO SEX

The Birds and The Bees

For many people, going to University is as much about meeting Mr or Mrs Right as it is about getting a degree. This isn't to say people are shallow – there is plenty of time for both. But the dating game is not simple and there is a lot of room for mistakes, hurt and regrets.

The Facts

A large percentage of people meet their 'life partner' at University – others include those who keep going steady with their childhood sweetheart, or those who don't settle down until their early thirties. These three traditional peaks are being added to by people who are partners-but-not-married, people who marry again later in life and people who never commit legally. What this means is that there is no normal time to meet.

Also, even among those who do meet at University, some will have had many previous boy/girl-friends and some will have had none. Some will be looking for a long term relationship, others for companionship and still more for something that fits right now with not too much thought about the future. Again, there is no standard agenda.

Because of this variety, there needs to be a lot of negotiation and compromise. The good news is that love is the best thing out there and can handle almost anything. The bad news is that most people either start off on the wrong foot, or don't keep working, negotiating and compromising.

Sex and Love

This needs to be clearly spelt out because people get the two confused so easily. Love is self-sacrificing, controlled, values the other person and gentle. People out for sex are none of these things. You may have heard these myths:

- You don't know if you love someone till you have slept with them

- If you loved me/found me attractive, you would sleep with me

- I have slept with lots of girls so I am a good lover

- People think about sex all the time so what's the problem

These are all things said when the person is not secure enough in themselves that they need to use sex to control, boast or boost their own confidence. I would go further and say you are probably not ready for sex until you do not need it for these reasons. For Christians, this means that sex is best placed within a loving and long-term commitment called marriage. It is there for its protection (and **your** protection) because it is an amazing thing and something to be respected. Sex without love causes:

- Images you will later regret of past sexual acts

- A bit of you broken off and forever with that person

- A reduce ability to enjoy good sex when you are ready

If you are being pressured into sex, please say No and remember that that person is probably not ready for it either if they are pressuring you. If you are currently in a sexual relationship, please know that it is not too late and ALL THINGS can be redeemed by God. Talk to someone – you will have to change but it will be worth it in the end.

Right is Right

Last century a chap called GK Chesterton said that 'right is right even when no body is doing it and wrong is wrong even when everybody is doing it.' To follow the kind of sexual ethic we have been talking about – and that means words like 'monogamy' and terms like 'no sex outside marriage' will land you firmly in a small minority at University.

Ever since the 'sexual revolution' of the 1960s, these views have been seen as outdated and wrong. The problem with the revolution was that it didn't bring freedom as promised. It did highlight some problems, like the Victorian women who were being raped within marriage, but it brought with it so many more difficulties and pain. Since that time the rates of sexual addiction, divorce, adoption, miscarriage and rape have been rising, not falling.

The number of people who 'live happily ever after' seems to be vanishingly small. But they do exist and we should be asking them what they are doing. Many [not all] are people of faith, and they will tell you things that you probably don't want to hear like not to rush into relationships, that it's best to wait till marriage before making love and that you frequently need to avert your eyes and walk in the other direction.

Not everything is relative

The problem with living like this is that people will tell you that this is just an opinion and their way is just as right, despite the evidence above that the sexual revolution has been far from effective. But they are right up to a point – it is just your word against their word. Or is it?

When two people disagree and both insist they are right, the argument is going to go nowhere without an external voice. The voice of popular culture is there, but this is just another bunch of humans who are all arguing from their own armchairs, their own limited experience and their own blinkered view of the evidence. As Christians, we can look outside the moral maze to an external voice that is unchanging, is objective and has the added benefit of being the Creator of the Universe and therefore all knowing and right!

We should be asking what God's views are. They will seem old-fashioned, but old-fashioned is sometimes good. And you will be in good company with me and many other Christian students across the world.

Staying on track

To keep true to God's plans for sex and relationships will mean swimming against the current and this is far easier when you are not doing it alone. Here are some tips for sticking to what you know is right:

- Be accountable with a couple of good friends. This is more than just sharing what is going though your head, it also involves being committed to obeying them if they tell you that you are going off track. £100 in a kitty should do the trick – you get it back at the end of each term!

- Keep up with the basics like going to church and being an active part of your cell group. Keep up with reading the Bible, telling people about Jesus and worshipping God – make these things big in your life so that the problem of temptation becomes smaller by comparison.

- If you do end up going out with / snogging / sleeping with someone you wish you had not, then do something about it quickly rather than letting it drag on and on when you know it is not going to work.

Dating and Christians

Common Question: Do I have to date someone who is a Christian?

The best rule is to look for someone who has the same ideals as you in terms of what the relationship is for and not for. The best foundation for this is to find someone who shares your values and hopes. For someone who is a Christian, this means going out with someone who is also a Christian.

There – I have said it! This isn't because I believe in stifling rules, but because I genuinely believe this to be the best foundation. The Bible is also clear that it is God's plan for you.

Even more vital than finding someone who shares your faith is finding someone who shares your PACE of faith. One great piece of advice I was given is, "Run as fast as you can towards Jesus, and from time to time look to the side. If you see someone who you fancy AND who is running the same speed as you, ask them out for a drink!"

Common Follow-up Question: What about 'flirt to convert'?

I have heard a lot of happy tales about people who have started dating someone who is not a Christian and that person has become interested in faith, started coming to church and given their life to God. However I have heard many, many more tales of people who have lost their own faith, dropped out of church and been unhappy. Sometimes years later they may come back to church and they all say that it was the worst thing they ever did. You chose what is wise...

If you do have strong feelings for someone who is not a Christian, you have two sensible choices. First is to tell your feelings to go away and be in control of them – it is a Hollywood fallacy that we are all at the mercy of every feeling. Second, you can have a very clear line about how far you are willing to go to see if that person does indeed take an interest in Jesus. Maybe a date or two – but be accountable, be careful with your heart and be strong.

Ending a long term relationship

There may come a time when you feel that the relationship you are in is not the right one. This may be because there are things that are definitely wrong, such as that one or both of you has a major issue with commitment, one of you is seeing someone else or even he/she is beating you. However, it may also be that things are just not working out any more – and this can often be the case with relationships that start at or before Uni, which statistically are many years before the average age people get married.

Endings are always hard so here are some ideas to help:

- If you can, break up amicably. It is unlikely you will be good friends as you have been to close so don't set this goal. It is good if it happens, but no more.

- When you break up, this means you break up. You no longer have power or rights over each other. You no longer need to confide or receive confidences. You do not have to reply to texts or phone calls.

- Try to learn what the problem was. It may not have worked this time, but you may be able to do things differently with the next person.

- Have an amnesty of stuff/jumpers/CDs. Do this as a one-off and don't keep ringing the door bell for this or that.

- Plan some things to do with your other friends, or join a new club if you have shared friends. Don't sit in and cry if you can help it.

- Make a 'So What' CD and play it LOUDLY! You can shout at God too – He can take it and will still love you.

- Remember that this is not the end, even though it feels like it is. You are young. There are plenty more fish in the sea…

Singleness ⬈ ⬅

Gone are the days when everybody grew up and got married. Actually they never existed, but nowadays some people are single by choice, others find themselves single in middle age after divorce, and yet more remain single till much later in life. At University, it can seem like everyone is dating and holding hands, so being single (especially if you don't want to be) can be hard.

Expectations

Many people come to University hoping to find that special person – and some do. However, some people have such high expectations that it becomes the all-consuming focus of those years, at the expense of study, having fun and other types of relationship. Some people do find 'the one' and get married soon after Uni, but there are far more who meet their special person later and settle down around age 30.

When the 'right person' does seem to appear, high expectations can mean you talk about marriage before they have ordered their starter and they run a mile. You have probably been thinking about them for weeks, so your heart gets broken and you blame them – but actually they have done nothing wrong. In fact, if you commit to having fun and forget about relationships for a while you are probably more likely to be seen as attractive – you will be more relaxed, eat better and come across as less weird.

Social networking

I love Facebook and, although you are asked to declare your relationship status, generally I am quite encouraged by the messy but fairly healthy data it conveys. There is a real mix of love and loss, new starts and 'same old'. However, other websites are about nothing but finding Mr or Mrs Right. There is huge pressure to get a partner at some point, fuelled as well by worries that people will think you are gay.

There are lots of websites that will claim to find you the right partner. I'm not just talking about Facebook, although you are encouraged to declare your relationship status on this. Some speciality sites will take your money [no obligation and guaranteed satisfaction, of course!], lead you up the garden path and introduce you to people who are seeking for all the wrong reasons. Some are specifically for Christians and promote the idea that one part of our faith is all about finding that special person God has laid out for you…

I do know people who have found love online, but they are few and far between and were often seeking in other ways too or actually had forgotten they had signed up! Please be wise, be cautious and be careful.

God's view of singleness

Because there is so much talk about marriage being a blessing from God, people who are single can end up feeling like second-class citizens. Marriage is a blessing, but this does not mean that the opposite is a curse. The only time singleness is a curse is when people make you feel awful for being single, especially if that is not your choice or wish. The cheek of this is that some of the most famous Christians of all were single – take Jesus Christ, St Paul and John Stott for starters.

Today's society is actually quite geared up to people being single. Organised social structures like churches are not quite so good – here there can easily be a division into those who are with someone and those who are not. Sometimes there are even special groups for these divisions. Jesus hung out with a whole bunch of people – of varying states of being – and I don't get the impression that he had his married disciples round one night for a dinner party then went to the pub with the single disciples. Perhaps we can learn to be better at and more comfortable with diversity. There are enough boundaries in life – lets not introduce some unnecessary ones.

Loneliness

A small minority are single by choice, and they often quote 1 Corinthians 7v7 an exhortation to be 'single for the Lord' and they do have a point – you have far more time as a single person and can travel more freely. However, the verse also makes it clear that some people can stomach this and others can't. The balance of the Bible is that most seem to desire to be 'with someone' and it sucks when they aren't.

Loneliness is a really aching feeling – made all the worse by the fact that you probably can't really talk to anyone about it to your satisfaction. However, there are some things to remember.

- You can start to assume you are the only one who feels like this, so it is worth talking to someone. However, make sure you don't end up in a mutual pit of despair

- The feeling will pass to some degree. It's just hard right now 'cos it's Saturday night and it seems like everyone else is out having fun. Bridget Jones moments are just moments.

- Loneliness as a single person sucks, but it is better than being lonely in a relationship, so please don't go out with anyone/thing just so you can say you have a date.

- Lonely is not the same as being alone. It is possible to be at peace and alone, just as it is possible to feel lonely at a busy party.

Living as a single person

- Have both singles and couples as friends, and mix them up with a party or two! This is just as true of people who are in relationships – we all need a range of friends and acquaintances

- Date occasionally – you have to kiss a few frogs before one of them will turn into your prince. But guard your heart. Take time with a potential relationship for both of your benefits

- Have fun. University is a wonderful time and there is plenty of time to have fun, as well as keep your eyes open for you know who.

Book Recommendation
The Single Issue, Al Hsu
Intervarsity Press ISBN 9780851111940

Masturbation and Pornography

Why is there a page on masturbation in this booklet – after all, isn't it harmless and isn't everyone doing it? The answer is that everyone does it, but a few are trapped by it, many are dulled by it and some Christians have very unhelpful perspectives on it.

By way of definition, masturbation is sexual stimulation which may or may not involve orgasm and is typically accompanied by creative or imitative images. Sometimes, it is just stimulating yourself to release tension and [for men] sperm, and if this were all that happened then we would not be writing this page. But our concern is as much for what goes on in your hearts and minds as below the belt. And this page is also for women.

Another description of masturbation is 'solo sex' – ie, sex with just yourself present. This often leads to the quip that masturbation is having sex with someone you respect, and this in itself shows why this way of thinking is a problem. If you are having sex with someone you don't respect then there is clearly something lacking in your understanding if sex – what it is, when it is for and why it is so much fun [animals don't do it half as much as humans] – see page 77 for a discussion on sex.

Stuff you will read on websites about masturbation:

- Something you need to do or your balls will explode [some think literally]

- It gives you hairs on the palms of your hands / sends you insane

- Masturbation is a harmless way of exploring your body

- You stop when you get married or start having 'real sex'

- Masturbation is something your partner is unconcerned about

The first two of these are complete myths and have been put about by people who seem to know little about masturbation or sex. These are particularly unhelpful for people who masturbate infrequently and for whom the lust dynamic is not a major problem. Masturbation like this will not kill you, your faith or your relationships. To say any more would be to go well beyond anything the Bible says.

The next three 'myths' are also not true but are more concerning. A large proportion of people will find masturbation gets out of control at some point in their life and needs addressing. And why is it that people are worried about the person they love masturbating? The answer is that they may well not be thinking about the person they are in love with. Typically it is a fantasy blonde or 'Brad', who is perfect in everyway, asks for nothing in return and makes them feel in control. But these things are pipe-dreams - they are not the reality of real relationships [even the good ones] – these are with imperfect people, a two-way street and both parties have to give up being the boss. To regularly go to a place in your head where you are in complete control will mean that over time you treat others poorly, deal less well with setbacks and the behaviour will increase as the problems increase.

Tips to change

When masturbation has become a problem, there are a number of ways to deal with it. Simple behavioural change techniques are a good place to start. However as well as cutting down the negative behaviour, we need to increase positive behaviours. We may also need to talk to someone:

- Twice a day is better that four times a day. Cut down, even if just a bit

- Practice healthy relationships – both platonic and exclusive

- Be accountable with a fellow student – but don't give people guilt trips. Accountability is about more than just saying how many times you have masturbated or ogled a short skirt – it is about purposefully building deep relationships where tough questions are asked and fun is had

- If it is damaging your relationships, consider getting specific help/prayer/counselling

Same-Sex Attraction

Being attracted to people of the same sex is an important topic to cover in a booklet like this, but a controversial one. Some will be offended that this is seen as a issue as they believe that all sexualities are equally valid and would say that this is no more a topic than heterosexual attraction. Well, you have just read a few pages about that, so here is one about homosexual attraction! For others, they will be offended from the other end of the spectrum - that this they believe that homosexual feelings are at odds with God's plan and that should be clear to everyone. Well, it may not be clear to everyone and even if it is that may not make it easy to bear. So this page exists because:

Same-sex attraction usually means fraught emotions

This may be because you have never ever told anyone how you feel and don't know where to start. It may be because if you did tell anyone you would fear rejection, because you fear the reaction of your parents / church / friends / current heterosexual boy-girl friend. Whatever the cause of the silence, it is clear to us that silence hurts and encouraging suffering in silence is not a Christian response, so here are some things you might like to contemplate. With a small but significant percentage of the UK population identifying themselves as gay, this is something we must talk about.

God has a view but that doesn't mean he hates people

We are not going to write classic old chestnuts here about what the Bible does and doesn't say – there is not enough room to do this justice and you can follow some of the links below to read more. However, we do want to be clear that a) God sets up heterosexual relationships as the norm and that b) homosexual acts are not permitted. Within these two parameters, there is a HUGE amount of ground and an equally huge number of opinions. It's unlikely that any one perspective is completely right, so please remember this when reading. Also, please remember that God loves you unconditionally and this is irrespective of current sexuality; and of past sexual sins [of any type!] that you have committed as these have been forgiven!

Some things to ponder

- There are people who are attracted to the same sex who are doing OK as Christians. Some are leaders, some are married, some are not. This is not an insurmountable or uncommon issue. Others have considered this before.

- This is something that can be talked about, but consider carefully who you want to talk to. However we would suggest you talk to someone wise at your church – they are probably not so squeaky clean as you think and have probably spoken to people about this issue before.

- 'Change' is possible. There is a lot of debate from both the Gay Rights Movement and scientific researchers about to what extent this can happen and it is true that many people will continue to have same-sex attraction to some degree. There are many testimonies to read and the book below contains the full range.

- It is neither your fault nor God's fault that you have these feelings. It may be obvious reasons where these feelings came from, or there may be nothing in your past at all. This is complex and blaming people will usually make things worse. However, don't hide your anger from God – He can take it and would rather you spoke to Him openly even if He is not responsible.

Resources

Book Recommendation
What some of you were
The Good Book Company, www.goodbook.co.uk ISBN 9781876326418

Web Sites
True Freedom Trust www.truefreedomtrust.co.uk
Living Waters www.living-waters-uk.org

Seeking Support
SOMEONE IS OUT THERE

Main Stream Websites

Student Counselling	www.student.counselling.co.uk [note the extra fullstop]	A good place to start for info and help. Run by all the University Counselling Services nationally
Student Depression	www.studentdepression.org	Award-winning site for depression with testimonies, examples and links to support
The NHS	www.nhs24.nhs	For urgent help and a place to visit if you are feeling suicidal. See more about the NHS on page 93
Mind – the national mental health charity	www.mind.org.uk	Full range of articles from a range of perspectives, especially people who have been mentally ill
Royal College of Psychiatrists	www.rcpysch.ac.uk	National body for psychiatrists in the UK. Research and academic content, but also some great leaflets for the public

Christian Websites

Association of Christian Counsellors	www.acc-uk.org	Find a Christian Counsellor near you. How to train in counselling
Anorexia and Bulimia Care	www.anorexiabulimiacare.co.uk	National Christian charity for eating disorders
Mind and Soul	www.mindandsoul.info	The people behind this booklet, their site has articles, podcasts, databases, events and lots more links like these. See page 92 for more
Premier Lifeline	www.premier.org.uk/lifeline	Anonymous confidential phone and email support for Christian advice and prayer

 Disclaimer: We cannot vouch for the content of other websites, but these websites are all generally thought to be trustworthy.

Your University

Your place of study has an interest in getting you to the end of your degree course and with a good grade. They have given you a valuable place, they want to give you a degree and they want you to go and tell others how great the experience there was. This means that they are investing in services to help you and support you – even if you think they only care about their research, alumni or income from fees! Here are some things you should find in most Universities.

University Counselling Service

Often staffed by several very experienced counsellors, they can be a one-stop-shop for most emotional difficulties. They have seen most things before, have good handouts on common problems on their website and are usually situated in a discreet corner of the campus where you can pop in unnoticed.

They can liaise with your academic tutors on your behalf and get you help if needed from local GPs and Mental Health Services. They can offer appointments quickly during term time. They may even offer support by email. They know all the local options in town, in the voluntary sector and who's in the know when stuff needs to get sorted. Drop in.

Student Services

The big wide world has social services. Universities have Student Services. These people will help you with finances, hardship grants, benefits, accommodation, academic difficulties and more. Many of the staff will be experts in disability – what help you can get and what rights and responsibilities you have.

There is a legal framework behind what they do called SENDA [Special Education, Needs and Disabilities Act, 2001] which requires a University to meet the needs of the students who attend. This does mean you have to declare the need in order for them to meet it. 'Needs 'include mental illness and autistic spectrum disorders as well as physical disability. Tell them and you might get a nice surprise!

Study Centre

Some students are academic machines and exam maestros. Others haven't written an essay in years, or have never learnt how to write one in the first place. Does maths muddle you? Does grammar garble you? If your basic study skills are letting you down, they can help with courses, groups, revision aids and peer group support.

Having marked hundreds of exam scripts, I can tell you that a coherent, structured and legible answer will get you a long way and set off your few facts to their best advantage. Most examiners can't be bothered to look for good content in poor clothing.

Mind and Soul

Mind and Soul is a national networking, equipping and encouraging organisation for people who are interested in how Christianity and Mental Health Problems relate. They are also the guys behind this booklet along with Fusion.

Mind & Soul
EXPLORING CHRISTIANITY AND MENTAL HEALTH
A Premier Lifeline Resource

We have three main aims – to link up people across the UK who are interested in Christianity and Mental Health, to put together high quality resources for the church on this topic and to share information about what is already going on near you.

Some of our resources are:

- A regular Podcast you can listen to online or through iTunes

- Major annual conferences with high quality speakers and seminars

- Databases of Christian Counsellors, Mental Health Projects and Mental Health Friendly Churches across the UK

- Articles on a wide range of topics with polls, forums and comments

- Regular emails highlighting new our audio and video archive

- Free confidential Christian email/phone counselling through Premier Lifeline

www.mindandsoul.info

Mind and Soul is part of Premier Christian Media – including Premier Christian Radio, Christianity and Youthworker magazines, Premier Life and Premier Community

Premier Christian Radio

Get us Nationally on DAB radio, Sky Digital 0123, Freeview 725, or in London on 1305, 1332, 1413 MW.

WWW.PREMIERRADIO.ORG.UK

Premier Lifeline

365 days of the year, 9am till midnight, 08456 525252 [lo-call rate]

WWW.PREMIER.ORG.UK/LIFE/LIFELINE

LIFELINE@PREMIER.ORG.UK

NHS

The NHS is the best state healthcare system in the world and the envy of many other nations. It is free to all who live in the UK, or who have a Visa [eg, if you are an overseas student], But it is a big beast – so here are some things to help you understand it.

Primary Care

This is what happens in your local health centre – many universities will have one they work closely with. There will be a number of GPs [General Practitioners, who are doctors] and a range of other health care workers like nurses, midwives, health visitors and maybe a counsellor.

- Everyone in the UK can be and should be registered with a GP. If you are a student away from home, you can have two GPs – one with your family and one at university

Secondary Care

This is mainly what happens at the hospital and includes things like A&E, investigative services like X-Ray and Labs for blood tests and also a long list of other specialities like orthopaedics, paediatrics, neurology, gastroenterology, etc, etc... Your GP will know who to refer you to for each problem and how long this will take. You will not always see a doctor – many specialities use senior nurses or other professions as your point of contact.

Emergency or Routine

For you, everything is urgent, but there are clear guidelines about what counts as an emergency and what means you have to wait. You may want your gammy knee fixed before the next rugby season, but this probably not a priority for the nation. There is a government target for all referrals to be seen within 18 weeks, so even routine cases should not take too long. You can look at www.nice.org.uk to see the hundred or so guidelines the NHS follows.

Private Healthcare

You may have access to this through your family [for example your parents' place of work], or you may chose if you have the money to pay for each visit. This is usually done at small private hospitals away from the main NHS sites; however it is typically the same doctors - who do their private work in the evenings or at weekend.

- You should always approach your GP to make a referral for private healthcare and never find someone in a phone book. Your GP may charge for this, but it is worth it – if you are going to pay you may as well see the best person locally.

Tips for students

Don't put off getting help just because you are at University. You can ask for an appointment during term times and you WILL get to the top of the waiting list before you leave Uni! You will be far busier after Uni and that is not the time to address health concerns. Sometimes there are special services for students such as a sexual health clinic or mental health team – ask your GP.

[fusion]

The ministry of Fusion emerged in 1997 as a response to a shared vision across the body of Christ to address the challenges of a changing student world. God's passion is for a dynamic student movement, one that will see Universities and Colleges won for Christ.

The Student Landscape:

- Recent figures suggest that there are 2.3 million students in the UK

- Student numbers have increased over 700% in the last 40 years and the government has set a target of 50% of all young people in Higher Education

- Less than 2% of students are actively involved in church

Our Mission

Fusion's mission is to reach every student with the gospel, initially in the UK and then beyond.

Our Purposes

Fuelling the fires of a national student movement through:

WORKING WITH STUDENTS: facilitating mission, evangelism and discipleship

SERVING CHURCHES: catalysing and helping to build local church-based student work

DEVELOPING STUDENT WORKERS: training and resourcing all those in student ministry

Our Values

Fusion's values are: Relational, Biblical, Missional, Catalytic and Inclusive

[fusion]

Other Resources available from Fusion include:

STUDENTSCAPE – a discipleship resource for new students

THE STUDENT ALPHABET – An A-Z of starting Uni

'LOVE YOUR UNI' – a guide to 21st century student mission

STUDENT LINKUP – preparing, resourcing and connecting new students

For more information on the work of Fusion contact us at:

The Fusion Office:

The Revelation Centre, Spur Road, Chichester, PO19 8PR

t: 01243 771405

e: office@fusion.uk.com

w: www.fusion.uk.com